Printed in the United Kingdom by
Northern Bee Books, Scout Bottom Farm,
Mytholmroyd,
West Yorkshire HX7 5JS
01422 882751 – www.beebiz.com

ISBN 0-393-30879-0
Plants and Honey Bees,
by Dr. David Aston & Dr Sally Bucknall

First Published 2004
Reprinted 2009

set in 11pt Bembo

Plants and Honey Bees

An Introduction
to Their Relationships

by

David Aston and Sally Bucknall
illustrated by William Dando

PREFACE

This book is about the European honey, or hive bee, *Apis mellifera* and the flowers and plants it utilises in the British Isles. It is principally intended as an introduction for beekeepers to provide an insight into the relationships between bees and flowers. It is hoped, however, that gardeners, naturalists, entomologists, biologists, agriculturalists, horticulturalists and those interested in conservation will all find something of relevance to their interests.

Acknowledgements

It was my wife Dr Sally Bucknall who first suggested to me that beekeeping might be something that would interest me. This book could not have been written without her collaboration and critique.

The diagrams are the work of my uncle, William Dando, for which I thank him very much.

I would also like to acknowledge all those who have introduced me to and taught me about plants and animals and their relationships, and more recently the endless fascination of honey bees.

Lastly I would like to thank my publisher, Jeremy Burbidge, for his support and encouragement.

David Aston
Wressle
East Riding of Yorkshire
October 2004

Contents

List of Tables

List of Figures

Photographs

Introduction

RELATIONSHIPS

The relationship of bees and flowers is a close and interdependent one that has evolved over many millions of years. A good knowledge of this relationship not only helps beekeepers to ensure their honey bee colonies are healthy and productive, but also introduces the beekeeper to the fascinating world of plants, their form and function and the ways in which bees and plants have adapted for mutual benefit.

The majority of flowering plants need to be cross-fertilised to ensure genetic variation, and this involves the transfer of pollen (male gametes) from one plant to the receptive female sexual organs of another plant to fertilise the female gametes. Some plants, however, are capable of self-fertilisation and do not need the transfer of pollen between individual plants.

The evolutionary development of flowers enabled many plants to utilise insects and other vectors such as birds, moths and bats as agents to facilitate pollination. In order to attract these animals the flowers are usually brightly coloured, scented and offer pollen or nectar as a food reward for the visit. In some cases the flowers have become indispensable to the insects. The result is that the evolution of plants and insects has become closely linked; with flowers becoming adapted to maximise the chances of pollen transfer by the insect. The process is thus more reliable than wind pollination, and insect-pollinated plants do not need to produce as much pollen as wind-pollinated plants.

Historically, biology, the science of life and living organisms, has been subdivided into botany; the study of plant life, and zoology; the study of animal life. It is now considered that this simple classification is no longer appropriate and that viruses, bacteria, blue-green algae and possibly fungi should not be included in the plant kingdom as they once were; they are now established in their own kingdoms.

Taxonomy, or the study of the similarities and differences between plants, has led to a scheme of classification reflecting the affinities and relationships that exist between different types of plants.

This book uses the names of plant species as found in Stace (2nd edition 1997). Where recent changes have been made to the family name by taxonomists, the previous name is shown in brackets after the current name for the first time it occurs in the text e.g. Asteraceae (Compositae). Subsequently only the current name is shown. The common names for plants are used for easy reading and in the Plant Index these and their binomial Latin names and families are given for completeness. Technical terms used in the text are explained in the Glossary.

BEE BASICS

The Honey bee, *Apis mellifera*, belongs to the insect order Hymenoptera that also includes ants, wasps and sawflies.

Honey bees are social insects living in colonies that during the summer months can consist of more than 50,000 individuals. The majority of the bees are workers that under normal circumstances do not lay eggs. Egg-laying is carried out by the queen bee of which there is usually only one in a colony. The different roles, appearance and behaviour of queens and workers are not determined genetically, but by the food the bee larva receives. A larva developing in a worker - sized cell can be developed into a queen if the workers feed large quantities of a special form of brood food called royal jelly. Under certain conditions worker's ovaries can develop and eggs can be laid in the absence of a queen in a colony, but these eggs develop into stunted drones.

The drones or males develop from unfertilised eggs and thus have only one set of genetic material (haploid). There may be several hundred drones present in a colony during the spring and summer months, but they are usually not allowed to survive over the winter months. In late summer and autumn the drones are removed by the worker bees, either by stinging or expulsion from the hive, after which they die as they are unable to forage for themselves.

The genetic relationship of bees is interesting. The drone, being haploid, receives only genetic material from its mother, the queen. Workers, which are all female, receive genetic material both from the queen and one of the drones with which she has mated. Thus they have two sets of genetic material (diploid).

In colonies left undisturbed, virgin queens are produced in the spring and summer months as part of the swarming process. The virgin queen mates on the wing soon after she emerges from her queen cell and she will mate with a number of drones on each of several mating flights. After mating the spermatozoa that will fertilize the eggs are stored in the queen's spermatheca. Her mating flights fill up her spermatheca and this quantity of spermatazoa has to last her lifetime. The queen has the ability to 'decide' whether or not to allow an egg to be fertilised, and it is through this mechanism that workers (developed from fertilised eggs) and drones (developed from unfertilised eggs) are produced. Once the queen has completed her mating flights she does not emerge from the colony again until the following season, when she may leave

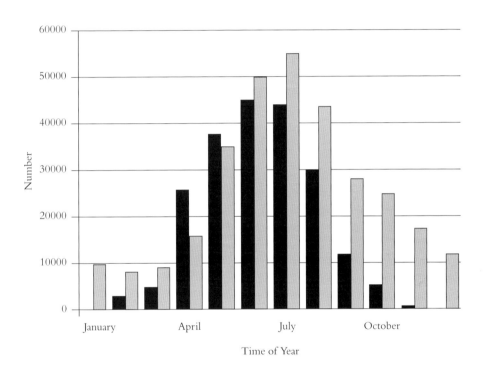

Figure 1. Annual population cycle of adults and brood in a honey bee colony.

as part of a swarm; the natural process by which colonies of bees reproduce. After swarming has taken place the original colony is left with a number of workers to tend developing worker brood. They also tend the virgin queens still in their queen cells until they emerge and fly to mate. Queen bees can live 4–5 years, but normal beekeeping practice is to replace queens in colonies every two years, sometimes annually.

Honey bees are totally vegetarian, eating plant-derived pollen for protein and nectar for energy; both collected by the workers. The nectar is stored in honeycombs in a concentrated form we call honey. Honey bees are generalists and will visit many species of plants in search of pollen and nectar. The workers also carry out the daily maintenance activities in the colony; regulate its environment; secrete wax; build comb; feed and care for the developing brood, and defend the colony.

Whilst honey bees are a wild species, humans have been able to harness bee's abilities for their own purposes. In general honey bees are manageable, adaptable, prolific and effective as pollinators for many agricultural crops, and vital to the pollination of many wild flowers. However, the majority of honey bee colonies only survive in the British Isles because of beekeepers. The main reason for this is a result of the impact of varroa *(Varroa destructor)*; a parasitic mite of honey bees first found in the British Isles in Torbay, Devon in 1992 having spread from Europe. Subsequently it has been found to be associated with bee viral diseases. Because of this, feral colonies usually die within 2–3 years of being established from swarms that are not recovered by beekeepers.

SEED-BEARING PLANTS

The most successful group of plants in evolutionary terms reproduce by means of seeds. They probably have their origin among extinct seed-producing members of the ferns and their close relatives. Seed-bearing plants are divided into several groups; the two main ones are commonly called angiosperms and conifers.

ANGIOSPERMOPHYTA (ANTHOPHYTA)

Flowering plants, also called angiosperms, evolved in the Cretaceous period around 135 million years ago, and eventually became the dominant land vegetation on a world scale, as different habitats were successfully colonised. Flowering plants share the following features:
- The reproductive organs are found within flowers.
- The ovules are enclosed in a protective structure called the ovary.
- They are seed-bearing, the seeds being formed as a result of fertilisation.
- The seeds are enclosed within fruits.

The angiosperms are divided into two major groups or classes known as monocotyledons (Monocotyledonae) and dicotyledons (Dicotyledonae) abbreviated for common usage as monocots and dicots. The main differences between the two groups are summarised in Table 1. (Page 6).

GYMNOSPERMS

The gymnosperms, a term no longer used in formal classification schemes, include cycads and conifers. The new terms are Cycadophyta and Coniferophyta respectively. These are also seed-bearing plants, but here the ovules are naked, not enclosed in an ovary, and are borne in cones.

HISTORY AND TAXONOMY

The science of plant taxonomy has two branches, the naming of plants (nomenclature) and the placing of plants into groups (systematics).

The correct identification of and reference to plants has always been of immense importance, as some could keep you alive, whilst others could make you or your stock very ill or even kill. For example, *Senecio jacobaea*, a common weed of road verges and neglected pasture, is known in various parts of the country as ragwort, ragweed, staggerwort, stinking billy, stinking weed or yellow weed. As a result of this someone from one area might not be understood in another area when referring to it by its local name, with unfortunate consequences.

The knowledge and folklore of herbal medicine held by practitioners was passed on orally or in the form of hand-produced illustrated herbals. The invention of printing made possible the publication of herbals, and their wider distribution increased access to the knowledge contained in them. The books by Grigson (1955) and Mabey (1996) contain interesting information on the folklore associated with plants and references to further source material.

The classification of plants was not seriously attempted until the 16th century. Up to this period botanical knowledge had scarcely advanced since the time of the classical writers such as Theophrastus (372? -287 BC) and Dioscorides (1st Century AD).

The Revival of Learning in the 16th century stimulated thought and the spirit of enquiry. Interested individuals and students of natural philosophy began to disentangle fact from fiction and plants were re-examined and careful descriptions and drawings were published. These were primarily intended to ensure the correct identification of those plants to which were attributed certain medicinal and therapeutic properties. Further searching, exploration and travel, greatly increased the number of known plants, and this continues in modern times.

Vegetative characteristics provided the basis for the earliest classification

Table 1 COMPARISONS OF THE CHARACTERISTICS OF DICOTYLEDONS AND MONOCOTYLEDONS

	DICOTYLEDONS	MONOCOTYLEDONS
Example	Peas, roses, buttercups, dandelion	Grasses, irises, orchids, lilies
Leaf morphology	Net-like pattern of veins (reticulate venation).	Veins are parallel (parallel venation)
	Lamina (blade) and petiole (leaf stalk)	Typically long and thin (grass-like)
	Dorsal and ventral surfaces differ	Similar dorsal and ventral surfaces
Seed morphology	Embryo has 2 cotyledons (seed leaves)	Embryo has one cotyledon.
Flowers	Parts★ mainly in fours and fives	Parts★ usually in threes.
	Petals and sepals are usually distinct	No distinct petals and sepals, parts combined to form perianth segments.
Type of pollination	Often-insect-pollinated	Often wind-pollinated

★ whorls of sepals, petals etc

6

systems, but these often led to incongruous results. It was Carolus Linnaeus (1707–1778), real name Carl von Linné, the Swedish naturalist who in 1735 used the characteristics of the sex organs (anthers and ovaries) to describe and classify twenty-four classes of plants. Subsequently these classes have been developed and changed to form the modern classification system.

An intellectually rigorous system of classification should be based on actual or demonstrable relationships, and it was the Doctrine of Descent, proposed by Charles Darwin in 1859, that provided a working hypothesis. He used his observations of morphological characteristics, through which affinities were suggested and the concept of phylogeny, or the evolutionary relationships of plants was built up.

It is possible to compare plants by taking into account all the morphological characters known about them. Those plants agreeing in the largest number of characters are usually regarded as being the most closely related from an evolutionary perspective. More recently these relationships have been further investigated biochemically, for example, the members of the Cabbage family produce similar essential oils that contribute to their taste as vegetables. Studies of the DNA of plants have also been used to refine the understanding of relationships.

In addition to the sexual system of classification, Linnaeus also developed a binomial system of naming plants. As the term implies two names are used to define an organism. The first is the generic (genus) and the second the specific (species) name. This system provides a universal name as a standard for organisms that may have popular names in different geographical areas and cultures, and plants are named in accordance with the International Code of Botanical Nomenclature. For many centuries the universal languages of scholarship were Greek and Latin and as a result Latin and Latinised versions of Greek words were used in the naming of plants.

The name of the genus is a collective name used to describe a group of plants having a number of characteristics in common. Within the genus, individual species are given a specific name that is often descriptive of the habitat where the plant is found, or relates to a particular morphological characteristic or use.

Some examples include:
- officinalis – of the apothecary; of use; of service to man
- angustifolium – narrow leaved
- fruticosus – bushy, shrubby
- vulgaris – common, ordinary
- pratensis – of the meadows
- odoratus – smelling
- repens – creeping

For example the genus *Ranunculus* (buttercups) contains a number of species named according to a characteristic of the plant e.g. *Ranunculus repens* (creeping buttercup), *R. bulbosus* (bulbous buttercup), *R. sceleratus* (celery-leaved buttercup). Within some closely related and superficially similar species a sub-division into subspecies and then into varieties is possible. As shown above, the genus name is often abbreviated to the first letter expressed as a capital followed by a full stop when plants of the same genus are listed. When written, binomial plant names are either written in italics or underlined.

Closely related genera, that share a general structural resemblance, are grouped together into families that are denoted by names ending in –aceae e.g. Ranunculaceae. Families are arranged in Orders.

The taxonomic hierarchy is based around the following divisions in descending order of size:

Kingdom/Phylum/Class/Order/Family/Genus/Species/Subspecies.

This classification is the basis on which botanical floras are constructed.

BOTANICAL FLORAS AND THE IDENTIFICATION OF PLANTS

Plant names in botanical floras include what appear to be abbreviations after them, e.g. in the name *Ranunculus repens* L. The letter L is an abbreviation of the name Linnaeus. The use of these abbreviations indicates the name of the first person to publish that name validly.

Botanical Floras contain dichotomous keys for the identification of plant species. They are constructed so as to lead the investigator through a sequence of choices between mutually exclusive character descriptions; each choice being binary and chosen to eliminate all but the specimen under observation. The series of questions to be answered relates to the presence or absence of observable morphological characteristics of the plant to be identified, usually the flower, to 'key out' the specimen. In some cases this may require the use of a x10 hand lens to see the flower parts and a sharp dissecting knife to cut the flower vertically or horizontally if required. Floras are written in a very dense technical shorthand jargon, and patience in working through the descriptions is rewarded with the pleasure of 'keying out' or identifying a specimen.

An example of a current flora is that of Stace (2nd edition 1997) in his 'New Flora of the British Isles'. A previous well-known flora was that of Clapham, Tutin, and Warburg, their 'Flora of the British Isles' was first published in 1952 with subsequent editions including field versions.

There are other ways of identifying flowers such as through coloured photographs or illustrations and their associated descriptions. These publications often group plants according to the colour of their flowers, or the habitat where they can be found, and this can be a very easy way to identify a plant; however, only by matching the description found in the flora can the identification be confirmed.

USING A FLORA

Before using a flora it is necessary to be able to identify the different parts of the flower, and to be familiar with the abbreviations used in the keys; these can usually be found in the front of the book. Once a plant has been chosen for identification it is important to observe it closely before starting to use the key, noticing in particular its habitat; stem woodiness; the variety of leaf shapes it exhibits; and the number, shape and arrangement of the floral parts. In the case of a plant that can be picked legally it is useful to collect flowers at various stages and fruits if possible; alternatively photographs may be taken for identification at a later time.

At the beginning of the key the choices can be made on easily observable features until the family level is identified. At this stage it can become more difficult, and it is important to read the description of the family characteristics that are found at the beginning of each family section. In large families there often will be a general key followed by sub-keys (e.g. Asteraceae) and when the genus level is reached it is again necessary to read carefully the introductory paragraph. When selecting one of two choices it is important to read the whole description of both options, and if in doubt, follow both, one will usually soon be seen to be a dead end.

At species level there is a full description of the plant including its growth habit; leaf shape; flower size, colour and arrangement; details of its sexual parts; its status (native or introduced etc.); its habitat, and its geographical location. If all these details match the specimen there can be no doubt as to its identity.

Care should be taken when examining plants in the wild. Many plant species now have a protected status and it is unlawful to pull up, cut flowers or collect seed from them without authorisation from statutory authorities. This does not mean that you cannot have a really close examination of the plants and the flowers in situ and enjoy finding out about them.

INTRODUCTION

Flower Structure

THE FLOWER, A SPECIALISED STRUCTURE

The flower, including the reproductive region of the plant, is usually distinctively delineated from the foliage or vegetative region. A flower may be single, whereas many flowers together on a single axis form an inflorescence.

A flower is defined technically as a specialised, determinate, reproductive shoot found in flowering plants that produces seed within it. It is a collection of essential organs, stamens or pistils or both, enclosed within a protective envelope.

Within all flowers different tissue cells produce male and female organs. A physical space exists between them and this barrier has to be overcome to enable sexual reproduction to take place through pollination, via the transfer of pollen from the anther (male parts) to a receptive stigma, (female parts).

The size of the space or gap depends on the location of the male and female organs in the species. For example, where male and female organs are on the same plant, but in different flowers, the plant is monoecious e.g. hazel. If the male and female organs occur on different plants they are dioecious e.g. holly and willow. When both sets of organs are present in the same flower on the same plant, the term is hermaphrodite or bisexual e.g. buttercup.

Understanding the structure of specific flowers gives an insight into their suitability as a pollen or nectar source for the honey bee, although flowers may be adapted to other specific types of pollinating agents, such as other insects, bats and birds.

THE INFLORESCENCE

The flower or inflorescence and the way it is borne on the plant is often a characteristic feature used in classification and identification. Sometimes the main vegetative axis of the plant ends in a single terminal flower, as in the case of the tulip and wood anemone, and the flower is said to be solitary and terminal. If present the stalk of the flower is called the pedicel and the flower is said to be pedicillate. If there is no pedicel, the flower is said to be sessile.

Table 2 THE MAIN TYPES OF INFLORESCENCE

TYPE OF INFLORESCENCE	EXAMPLES
Raceme	foxglove, hyacinth
Panicle	oat
Corymb	candytuft
Simple Umbel	carrot, onion
Compound Umbel	cow parsley
Capitulum	dandelion,
Dichasial Cyme	stitchwort, hellebore, buttercup
Monochasial Cyme	iris, forget-me-not
Catkin	hazel
Spike	orchid

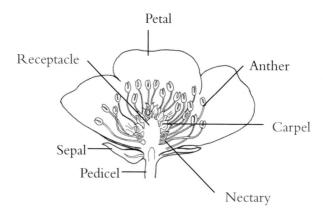

Figure 2. Longitudinal Section (LS) Buttercup *(Ranunculas spp.)* flower

Usually the flowers are aggregated on a more or less complex branch system and the inflorescences may then be described by the way they are arranged (Table 2). The structure, patterns, colours, and shapes of each type of inflorescence and flowering time are adapted to the pollinating vectors that the plant needs to attract in order to ensure pollination. Two kinds of structure, the androecium (male parts) and the gynoecium (female parts), are necessary for the performance of the reproductive function; but in some cases a flower may possess only one of them e.g. holly. Often a flower has other accessory characteristics, such as colour, that make it interesting both to people, and as an attractant to the insect or other vector that will transfer pollen from one plant to another to facilitate the production of seed.

The apex of the flower stalk is called the receptacle, also known as the thalamus or torus, and this bears the parts of the flower called the perianth, stamens and carpels (fig. 2).

THE PERIANTH

In many flowers the receptacle bears four sets or whorls of floral organs. The outer whorl of the flower consists of the sepals, collectively called the calyx. These may be joined together to form a calyx tube, and in the case of the dandelion the calyx has become modified into a group of hairs called a pappus (fig. 4, page 15). Above and within the calyx are the petals, usually brightly coloured and collectively called the corolla. Together the sepals and petals are called the perianth. In some plants bracts are present and these resemble a small leaf with a relatively undeveloped blade in the axil of which a flower, a branch or inflorescence can arise (fig. 3, page 15). Bracts are often green but they may be coloured like petals and in this instance they are said to be petaloid.

CALYX/SEPALS

The calyx protects the flower in its bud stage and may have a protective function at other times of its life, for example, during the flowering stage when it may prevent the thieving of nectar by non-pollinating insects from flowers that have nectaries deep seated in the corolla. The calyx may act as a 'corolla' serving to attract the pollinating vector. This is often the case when the petals themselves are transformed into tubular nectaries e.g. in hellebores or when the petals are reduced in size or absent e.g. in daphne.

The hellebore calyx is unusual; at first it is green and protective in function and then becomes coloured and attractive. As the seed follicles begin to ripen the calyx becomes green and softer again. It is persistent, dying only when the stem itself dies.

In the dead-nettle family, Lamiaceae (Labiatae), the calyx is persistent even when the fruits are ripe. In the marsh-marigold it is the sepals that are coloured;

the petals are absent and the perianth consists of one whorl of 5-8 petaloid sepals.

COROLLA/PETALS

Petals with their great variety of colour, size, shape and scent, act as the attraction for pollinators. The corolla may consist of free petals, or a single whorl as in the foxglove and geranium.

Garden varieties of plants are often bred for showiness with double or more whorls of petals or petaloid sepals; but these are usually of little interest to bees because the flowers may be sterile and produce little or no pollen or nectar. Plants grown to encourage insects should be chosen with this in mind.

The corolla may be polypetalous (free petals) or gamopetalous (fused petals). The symmetry of the flower may be either zygomorphic, where the flower can be bisected vertically in only one plane (bilaterally symmetrical), as in the sweet pea, or actinomorphic where the flower can be bisected vertically into two or more similar planes (radially symmetrical), e.g. buttercup.

If the petals are joined together the joined portion is called the corolla tube and the free parts are called corolla lobes. The corolla tube may act as a nectar reservoir and the texture of the petals and/or the presence of hairs can be important in their effectiveness in the retention of nectar. If the petals are green they are described as sepaloid (like sepals). In some cases the sepals and petals are similar in colour and shape e.g. tulip, and in this case the perianth segments are called tepals.

In some flowers there are intermediate stages between petals and stamens, petals may bear an anther sac or there may be petaloid stamens. This is common in the rose family, Rosaceae, e.g. hawthorn. The corolla may have additional appendages and these are called coronas. The yellow corona of the forget-me-not and the blue of the petals is a recognisable contrast for the visual perception of the honey bee. In many flowers the sepals and petals are short-lived, shrivelling at the time of anther dehiscence or when pollination has occurred.

ANDROECIUM

The Androecium is the collective term for the stamens or male sex organs of the flower. A stamen consists of three parts, filament, anther and connective. The filament is the stalk of the stamen supporting the anther. The anther has two (usually) or four lobes, and within each lobe is a layer of cells that nourishes the microspores (pollen grains). Pollen grains are similar in function to sperm in animals. The pollen grains lie in four cavities, the pollen sacs, of which there are two in each lobe. The anther lobes are connected and separated by a strip of tissue called the connective.

The anther filament can be attached to the base of the anther (basifixed) or the back (dorsifixed) and in both cases the anther may be immovable; however

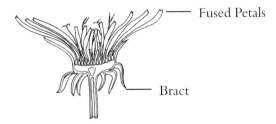

Fused Petals

Bract

Figure 3. LS Dandelion
(Taraxacum officinalis) capitulum

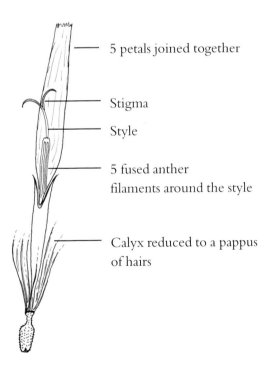

5 petals joined together

Stigma

Style

5 fused anther
filaments around the style

Calyx reduced to a pappus
of hairs

Figure 4. Single floret from
a Dandelion capitulum

some filaments bend at their apex so that the anther swings on the filament, and in this case they are called pendulous or versatile. Versatile and pendulous anthers are frequently found in wind-pollinated flowers e.g. grasses (Gramineae).

The stamens may be attached below, around or above the ovary, or to the perianth or the corolla as is found in the Asteraceae (Compositae), e.g. dandelion; Lamiaceae, e.g. dead-nettle, and Primulaceae, e.g. primrose. They may be attached at the base only, i.e. they are free, as in Ranunculaceae, e.g. buttercup, or they may be united to form a tube as is the case in the Malvaceae e.g. mallow.

Stamens may be of different lengths in a flower. In the Brassicaceae (Cruciferae) e.g. wallflower and oil-seed rape, there are four long and two short stamens; whilst in the Lamiaceae e.g. the dead-nettles, there are two long and two short stamens. Barren or rudimentary stamens are called staminodes; these are often found in cultivated varieties of plants.

All of these variations have significance for the way in which the pollen is presented to the visiting insect. In some species of the Lamiaceae the flowers actively deposit pollen on the bee as it enters the flower. In the case of the Papaveraceae e.g. field poppy and members of the Asteraceae e.g. the dandelion, the flowers are passive and the bee scuffles over the flower surface collecting the pollen.

GYNOECIUM

The gynoecium is the collective term for the carpels of a flower i.e. the female sex organs. Most plants have a gynoecium consisting of a number of carpels, however, in some species e.g. broad bean, the gynoecium consists of a single carpel or pistil. Each carpel typically consists of a style, a stigma and an ovary containing one or more ovules that become seeds after fertilisation. These ovules equate to the eggs or ova in animals. At or near the top of the style is the stigma, receptive to and on which the pollen grains stick. The stigma usually arises from the apex of the ovary, but in some families e.g. Lamiaceae, it arises from the base.

The relationship of the gynoecium to the receptacle determines whether the carpels are inferior or superior, and this is important when understanding the origins of the fruits and seeds that plants develop. When the carpels are located in the base of a conical receptacle and other flower parts are inserted in turn below, the gynoecium is superior and the flower is said to be hypogynous e.g. campion. When the carpels are at the centre of a concave receptacle, with the other floral parts borne around its margin, the gynoecium is superior and the flower is perigynous e.g. roses (rosehips), strawberry and raspberry. In perigynous flowers the wall of the receptacle remains distinct from the ovary.

When the receptacle completely encloses the carpels and other floral parts

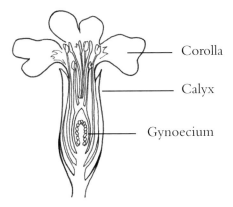

Figure 5. LS Campion *(Silene spp.)*
flower parts hypogynous
i.e. inserted below the gynoecium

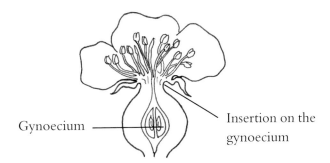

Figure 6. LS Pear *(Pyrus spp.)* flower parts
epigynous i.e. sepals, petals and stamens are
inserted on the gynoecium

arise from the top of the receptacle, the gynoecium is inferior and the flower is said to be epigynous e.g. pear. In epigynous flowers the floral parts arise from or are inserted on the gynoecium.

The wall of the ovary develops into the pericarp of the fruit and this may be dry and membranous, as in the case of a nut, or fleshy as in a berry. The ovule is covered by a skin or integument and there is a minute opening in the integument known as the micropyle through which the pollen tube grows after pollination. It is also through the micropyle that water enters at the start of seed germination.

Some flowers contain nectaries that are fluid secreting tissues and are found especially in insect-pollinated flowers. This fluid is called nectar.

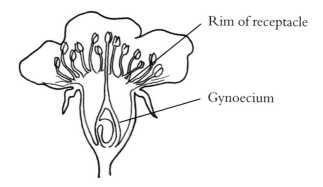

Rim of receptacle

Gynoecium

Figure 7. LS Cherry *(Prunus spp.)* flower parts perigynous i.e. the gynoecium develops in the cup of the receptacle with flower parts inserted on the rim of the receptacle

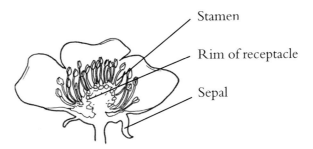

Stamen

Rim of receptacle

Sepal

Figure 8. LS Blackberry *(Rubus fruticosus)* flower parts perigynous with the sepals, petals and stamens around the rim of the receptacle, not underneath it

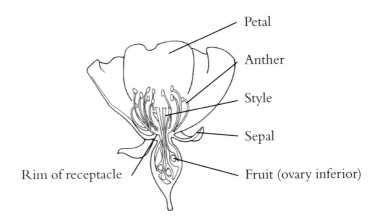

Petal

Anther

Style

Sepal

Rim of receptacle

Fruit (ovary inferior)

Figure 9. LS Wild rose *(Rosa spp.)* flower with the flower parts perigynous, i.e. inserted in the rim of the receptacle

Plate 1 Buttercup *(Ranunculus spp.)*.
Simple flower showing perianth, stamens and carpels.

Plate 2 Dandelion *(Taraxacum officinalis)*.
Compound flower head made up of many ray
and disc florets *(a capitulum)*.

Plate 3 Rose *(Rosa spp.)*. With the exception of the
Briar Rose, rose flowers only produce pollen.

Plate 4 Knapweed *(Centaurea spp.)*. Because of the
length of the corolla tube in the central disc florets,
nectar can only be accessed by long-tongued bees.

Plate 5 Holly *(Ilex aquifolium).* An example of a
dioecious species where the male and female flowers
are on different individuals. This picture shows
the male flowers.

Plate 6 Holly *(Ilex aquifolium.).* Female flowers after
fertilisation showing young green berries.

Plate 7 Bramble *(Rubus fruticosus).* A member of the family Rosaceae, typically an open flower with many stamens.

Plate 8 Oil–seed rape *(Brassica napus ssp. oleifera).* A typical member of the Brassicaceae with 4 sepals and 4 petals.

Plate 9 Hellebore *(Helleborus spp.)*,
showing tubular nectaries that are modified petals.

Plate 10 Broad bean *(Vicia faba)*. The dark blotches
on the stipules are extra-floral nectaries and
are attractive to bees, ants and aphids for the
nectar they secrete.

Plate 11 Ivy *(Hedera helix)* is a very valuable late source of nectar and pollen. The sugar concentration in the nectar can be so high that it crystallises on the flower as can be seen in this photograph.

Plate 12 Lime *(Tilia spp.)*, a close-up of an individual flower in a lime inflorescence.

Plate 13 Geranium *(Geranium spp.)*,
this flower shows the nectar guides which to the
human eye appear as dark lines on the petals.

Plate 14 Foxglove *(Digitalis purpurea)*,
here the nectar guides are seen as blotches on
the lower lip of the corolla.

Plate 15 Forget-me-not *(Myosotis ssp.)*, a member of the family Boraginaceae showing the typical raised yellowish coloured corona in the centre of the flower.

Plate 16 Astrantia *(Astrantia spp.)*. a member of the family Apiaceae with typical umbel flowers.

Plate 17 Purple dead–nettle *(Lamium purpureum)*. These flowers deposit their pollen on the backs of visiting insects, an example of nototribic pollination.

Plate 18 Broad Bean *(Vicia faba)*, these flowers open when the visiting bee triggers the keel petals to open and the pollen is deposited on the underside of the insect, an example of sternotribic pollination.

Plate 19 A worker honey bee performing
in-flight movements where she combs the pollen
down her rear legs depositing it in the pollen basket.
She has just visited an apple *(Malus spp.)* flower.

Plate 20 A foraging honey bee working a plum
flower. The pollen load in her pollen basket and the
pollen grains on her body can be seen.

Plate 21 Strawberry *(Fragaria spp.)* flower showing the large central receptacle that swells to form the fruit.

Plate 22 Strawberry *(Fragaria spp.)* flowers at the time of petal drop and the receptacle is starting to swell.

Plate 23 Strawberry *(Fragaria spp.)*,
the ripe fruit developed from the receptacle with
the seeds on the outside of the fruit.

Plate 24 Phacelia *(Phacelia tanacetifolia)*, a very
valuable source of pollen and nectar for all bee species,
it is planted in bee conservation schemes.

Nectaries

Nectaries consist of specialised groups of cells that secrete sugary fluids that attract the pollinating agent into the flower, e.g. the honey bee. Nectaries may be modified floral parts or extra-floral i.e. found outside the flower. When found within the flower the usual place for nectaries is at the base of the ovary where they frequently take the form of a raised ridge of secretory tissue, often yellow in colour. However, any part of the flower may be modified into a nectary or bear nectar secreting tissue.

TYPES OF NECTARIES
SEPAL NECTARIES

Examples of sepal nectaries are found in some members of the mallow family, Malvaceae, e.g. tree mallows. In the garden tree mallow each sepal bears a discreet patch of secreting tissue. Dense hairs fringe the bases of the petals and possibly prevent the entry of tiny insects too small to effect pollination, whilst allowing pollinating insects access to the nectar.

The flowers of various species of lime, Tiliaceae, also contain sepal nectaries, appearing as tiny slits of secreting tissue invisible to the naked eye. The boat-shaped sepals are lined with hairs, which assist in holding the drop of nectar as it forms in the hollow or inner surface of the sepal; this is important as the flower is generally in a pendant (hanging down) position (fig. 10 &11, page 23).

In some species of the Brassicaceae the sepals are bent back or curved and serve as nectar reservoirs. In this case nectar is not secreted by the sepals but by nectaries at the base of the ovary.

PETAL NECTARIES

In the hellebore, the true petals are modified into small tubes, these are found within the coloured, deltoid sepals. The lips of many of the true petals of the primary flowers of hellebores are pinched together and inaccessible to honey bees. As a result honey bees gathering pollen from the primary flowers in January/February visit lower flowers where two thirds of the tubular nectaries are accessible. The winter aconite, Ranunculaceae, has modified the whole true petal into a vase-like structure to secrete and hold the nectar.

Buttercup nectaries are situated under a tiny flap of tissue near the base of the petal. In the snowdrop the nectar is collected in grooves on the inner surface of the petals. In the Asteraceae, e.g. thistles, a small ring of nectar secreting tissue is found at the base of the tubular corolla and as the flower tube is narrow, nectar soon rises in the tube and becomes accessible to the honey bee.

STAMINAL NECTARIES

Nectar is secreted between the base of the stamen tube and the ovary in clover, Fabaceae (Papilionaceae / Leguminoseae), and it is then held by the tube formed by the stamens, and only becomes accessible to the honey bee when the level of nectar is high enough in the tube to be reached with its proboscis.

Members of the Violaceae have staminal nectaries in the form of two slender tongues of green tissue arising from the filaments of two of the stamens. They project backwards into the spurred petal that receives their secretion, although does not itself secrete nectar. Some of the nectar is accessible to the honey bee. The flowers of the wild clematis also have nectar secreting stamens and the nectar is produced in droplets on the anther filaments. In the Pasque flower, the anthers of a few of the outermost stamens secrete nectar instead of producing pollen.

CARPEL NECTARIES

There are three distinct types of carpel nectary, namely valve, septal and disc.

An example of the valve nectary is found in the marsh-marigold; it is a simple groove of secreting tissue on the sides and towards the base of the young carpel.

The septal nectary is typically found in members of the Liliaceae. For example, in bluebell the young ovary has three vertical grooves marking the position of the septa. Nectar is secreted along these lines, and appears as beads of nectar that run down the grooves and collects around the base of the ovary in the cup of the perianth, where it is accessible to the honey bee. Both the scabious and teasel secrete nectar from the ovary wall.

In the carrot family, Apiaceae (Umbelliferae), the inferior ovary is surmounted by a thick pad or disc nectary, often yellowish-green, consisting of secreting tissue through which the styles emerge. The nectar is freely exposed in this case. In the willowherb family, Onagraceae, the disc nectary is also on top of the ovary. The nectar of ivy, is secreted between September and November from a disc nectary, and although a very useful nectar source for over-wintering bees, it can crystallize in the flowers or, after storage, in the honeycomb and become unavailable to the bees.

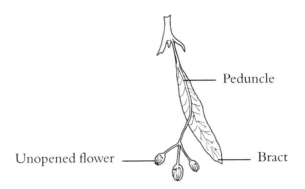

Figure 10. Inflorescence of Lime *(Tilia spp.)*

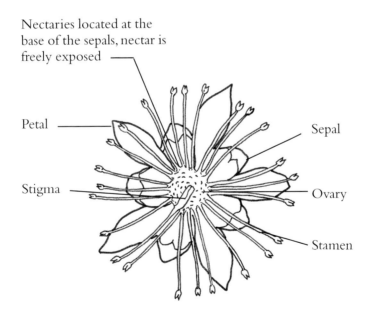

Figure 11. Single Lime Flower

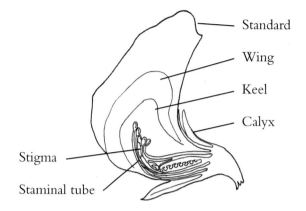

Standard

Wing

Keel

Calyx

Stigma

Staminal tube

Figure 12. LS Sweet Pea *(Lathyrus odoratus)*, flower typical
of the Fabaceae (Papilionaceae).

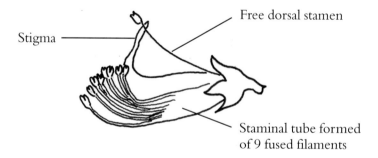

Stigma

Free dorsal stamen

Staminal tube formed
of 9 fused filaments

Figure 13. Sweet Pea *(Lathyrus odoratus)* flower petals
removed to show staminal tube.

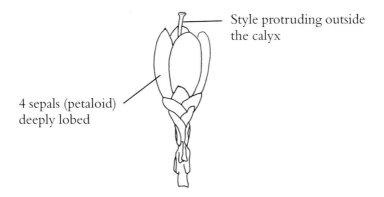

Style protruding outside
the calyx

4 sepals (petaloid)
deeply lobed

Figure 14. Ling heather *(Calluna vulgaris)* flower

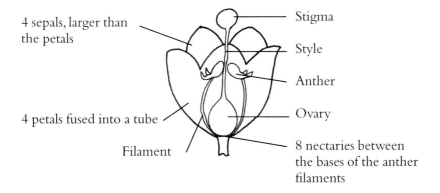

4 sepals, larger than
the petals

4 petals fused into a tube

Filament

Stigma

Style

Anther

Ovary

8 nectaries between
the bases of the anther
filaments

Figure 15. Ling heather half flower

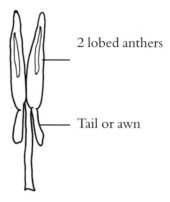

Figure 16. Ling heather anther

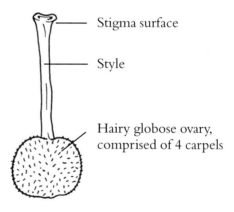

Figure 17. Ling heather ovary

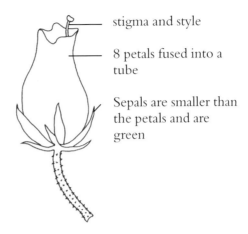

Figure 18. Bell heather *(Erica cinerea)* full flower

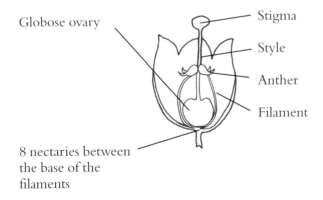

Figure 19. Bell heather *(Erica cinerea)* half flower

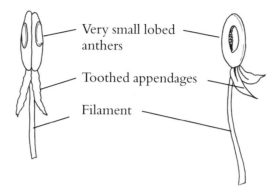

Figure 20. Bell heather *(Erica cinerea)* anther

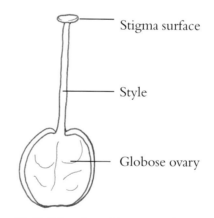

Figure 21. Bell heather *(Erica cinerea)* ovary

RECEPTACLE NECTARIES

In the members of the Rosaceae, such as the raspberry, blackberry, almond and plum, the receptacle-shaped cups of the perigynous flowers are lined with nectar secreting tissue. The open shape of the flower allows the honey bee to access the nectar.

AXIAL NECTARIES

In this type of nectary the secreting tissue is found around the base of the ovary. Examples can be found in the dead-nettle family, Lamiaceae.

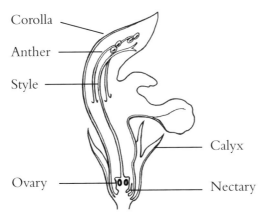

Figure 22. LS White dead-nettle
(Lamium album) flower

NECTAR SECRETION

The mechanism of nectar secretion is not fully understood but it is known to be dependent upon the metabolic activity of the nectary tissue and there may be several possible metabolic pathways. Nectar is secreted from the nectary cells into the intercellular spaces from which it diffuses through the epidermis and/ or stomata of the nectary tissue.

FACTORS AFFECTING NECTAR SECRETION
POSITION OF THE FLOWER ON THE PLANT

In phacelia the nectaries in the flowers at the bottom of the plant secrete more nectar than those at the top. Bramble flowers occurring on stout shoots secrete more nectar than those on thin shoots. In the case of rosebay willowherb, once the lower flowers on the main inflorescence have faded the bees do not seem to work the higher flowers in the inflorescence, moving to the lower flowers of other subsidiary flowering shoots.

THE AGE OF THE FLOWER

In bramble the amount of nectar produced by successive flowers on the same inflorescence decreases. In the case of ling heather, the moorland practice of heather burning to encourage new heather shoots for the management of grouse, results in a much greater nectar secretion from flowers on the young shoots compared to older, woody, heather plants that have not been burnt.

Bumble bees can work the prime or early summer flowers of red clover, and once these have been cut and the plant makes a second growth, usually at the end of August, honey bees are then able to work the smaller flowers because the corolla tube is shorter in the second growth and the nectar rises relatively higher in the tube and thus becomes accessible to them.

DIFFERENCES IN VARIETY AND SPECIES

In a study involving eight varieties of apple the daily nectar production between the varieties varied from 1.8 – 6.2 mg of sucrose per flower. Plants that secrete high levels of nectar include the large and small-leaved limes, clary sage, rosebay willowherb, gooseberry, and borage. These have all been recorded in Europe as secreting more than 3mg of sugar per flower in 24 hours.

SOLAR RADIATION

In clover and heaths nectar secretion is boosted on a sunny day and depressed on a dull day. Generally speaking small flowers, each secreting small amounts of nectar, are a feature of flowers of the northern temperate zones e.g. clovers and blackberry.

RELATIVE HUMIDITY

Nectar in deep tube flowers is largely protected from the external environment, whilst nectar in shallow open flowers is relatively unprotected and changes in relative humidity, rain or air movement may affect the sugar concentration in the nectar. Atmospheric humidity has a pronounced effect on nectar sugar concentration; as nectar is secreted, its concentration alters until its vapour pressure comes into equilibrium with that of the atmosphere. Unless the atmospheric humidity is very high the result will be a loss of water molecules from the nectar into the air and an increase in the sugar concentration of the nectar. This may radically affect the pollination potential for the flowers, as the more concentrated the nectar the more attractive it is to the honey bee.

SOIL MOISTURE

In temperate regions the level of soil moisture is seldom a limiting factor to nectar secretion unless it drops to a level where the plant wilts. However, it may be sub-optimal in its effect, when low water table levels and inadequate root depths may be limiting.

TEMPERATURE

Research has shown that temperature has a significant effect on nectar secretion, however, other factors such as geographical location, and crop plant variety, also cause differences in secreting levels showing that this may be much more complex than a direct relationship.

Flower development is accelerated at high temperatures, and the duration of nectar secretion is likely to be shortened. Excessively high temperatures in combination with low rainfall can lower nectar production by causing moisture stress in the plant. Research shows that below certain temperature thresholds plants will not secrete nectar, e.g. below 8°C in wild cherry and cherry laurel. White clover is most productive in cool air temperatures and can be bred for this, although it may also require a warm soil. Hawthorn only secretes well when the temperature is exceptionally high, at least 25°C during its flowering period. There is a beekeeper's old saying that 'Cool nights and warm or hot days promote the flow of nectar', but lime produces most nectar when the nights are warm and the days are sultry and humid. Some species, e.g. bramble, are not influenced by temperature and will continue flowering until cold weather and frosts.

PLANT NUTRITION

The nutritional status of the plant in the previous and current year is important to its flowering potential, and the vigour of the plant and its flowers influences the amount of pollen and nectar that is available for bee forage.

ACIDITY AND ALKALINITY OF SOIL

Soil pH is also important. Some plant species are very specific in terms of their pH tolerance range for acidity and alkalinity, and where they will grow most successfully. Better nectar yields for white clover occur on alkaline soils whereas heather yields best on acid soils. Some plants such as bramble and sycamore show a wide tolerance range and do equally well on acid or alkaline, light or heavy soils.

TIME OF DAY

As a general rule, and especially in the case of simple open access flowers, the sugar concentration of nectar is often weaker during the early part of the day and peaks later in the morning when the effects of heat and wind cause water evaporation and increase the sugar concentration in the nectar. Nectar quality and quantity do not necessarily coincide at the same time, and bees have the ability to evaluate the energy value of nectar. Bees will often switch from one nectar source to another as a result of changes in quality and/or quantity. For example, with apples often bees will work the flowers for pollen early in the day and return later in the day to collect nectar when it has become more concentrated and the energy value more worthwhile.

TOPOGRAPHY

Frost pockets and cold air drainage may damage or destroy flowers. Ling heather and white clover are thought to secrete more freely on sloping sites, but this may be influenced by other factors such as drainage, temperature, and soil aeration.

SHADING

Regardless of air temperature some plants only secrete well in sunshine, e.g. dandelion.

WIND

Mild drying winds after a period of rain can have a very beneficial effect on nectar secretion, whereas cold winds will not. As a general rule extremely dry weather or high winds with low temperatures result in low nectar secretion.

THE 'JUNE GAP'

Usually by late May and early June the nectar sources of fruit trees, sycamore, holly, hawthorn (in good years), horse-chestnut, and oil-seed rape are dwindling, and if field beans are not available there may be little nectar for large colonies. This is known as the June Gap. Beekeepers should be aware that honey and pollen stores in the colonies can be rapidly depleted at this time. Although there may be little available forage, plenty of space should continue to be given to colonies to reduce the amount of overcrowding which can promote the initiation of swarming. The June Gap may change or disappear as the impact of global warming and climate change affects the flowering times of plants.

EXTRA-FLORAL NECTARIES

Extra-floral nectaries, as their name suggests, are located outside the flower and may be on leaves, stipules, or stems. In the British Isles there are a number of plants that have extra-floral nectaries. In the cherry laurel, extra-floral nectaries can be found in the angle between the midrib and main veins on the back of the leaf. In beans and vetches, extra-floral nectaries occur in small depressions on the backs of the stipules. In these species nectar from floral and extra-floral nectaries is produced in sunny but not in dull weather. Although not a flowering plant, bracken has a smooth shiny nectary at the point where each pinna joins the rachis of the frond. These nectaries secrete abundant nectar and it is considered to be an important nectar source for bees in some upland parts of the British Isles when no other spring forage is available.

Historically many plants have been introduced into the British Isles and these may also have both floral and extra-floral nectaries. At present there is little information as to whether the extra-floral nectaries of these species are functional in the climatic conditions found in the British Isles. Examples include extra-floral nectaries on the stems and stipules of young American elderberry plants; the leaves of passion flowers; leaf lobes of peaches; pits on the petioles of trumpet vine and hairy vetch; flower buds of peonies; glandular trichomes (hairs) on lower leaf surfaces and the leaf stipules of false-acacia.

Questions have been asked as to the adaptive advantage of having extra-floral nectaries. One speculation is that they are found on plants that have no spines to protect them against herbivores, and it may be that the nectar produced attracts ants in particular. Ants may sting any animal attempting to eat the plant, thus protecting it.

Further information on nectaries can be found in Annex I.

NECTARIES

Nectar

NECTAR COMPOSITION

Nectar is water containing a number of dissolved substances that range between 3 and 87% of the total dry weight, and 90-95% of the total solid matter. It is usually acidic with a pH range of 2.7 - 6.4. The amount and sugar content of nectar is dependent on the plant species and the environment, especially weather conditions.

A typical nectar composition might be:

- Water 30-90% by weight.
- Sucrose 5-70% b/w.
- Fructose 5-30% b/w.
- Glucose 5-30% b/w.
- Other constituents up to 2% b/w.

More detailed analyses have identified the following substances in samples of nectar, although the composition varies depending on the plant source.

- Sugars: such as sucrose, glucose, fructose, xylose, raffinose, melezitose, trehalose, melibiose, maltose, dextrin, and rhamnose.
- Vitamins: principally vitamin C and some of the vitamin B complex.
- Amino acids: including aspartic acid, glutamic acid, serine, glycine, alanine (the most important to bees of 13 isolated from nectar samples).
- Minerals: e.g. potassium, calcium.
- Organic acids: e.g. gluconic and citric acids.
- Pigments.
- Aromatic compounds: e.g. alcohols and aldehydes.
- Enzymes: including invertase, transglucosidase, transfructosidase, tyrosinase, phosphatases, and oxidases.
- Mucus, gums, ethereal oils, and dextrin.
- Particulate constituents including pollen, fungi, yeasts and bacteria.
- Antioxidants mainly ascorbic acid (vitamin C).
- Occasionally lipids and alkaloids and proteins.

Nectars containing high levels of sugars tend to have higher levels of amino acids, detectable lipids and/or antioxidants. If alkaloids are present, these constituents plus protein are usually found.

The influence of the lesser ingredients becomes more obvious as water is evaporated from the nectar and it becomes more concentrated during conversion into honey. It is the concentrated constituents that give the aroma, taste and flavour to honey.

TYPES OF NECTAR

Nectars can be categorised into the following types:
- Sucrose dominated nectars associated with tube flowers and with protected nectaries.
- Fructose and glucose (with little sucrose) dominated nectars associated with open flowers and unprotected nectaries, and usually containing more fructose than glucose.
- Nectars containing roughly equal proportions of fructose, glucose, and sucrose (less common).

The type of nectar affects the granulation characteristics of the honey that is derived from it. It is sometimes a feature of the plant family as a whole, and closely related families have similar kinds of nectar. Pure sucrose dominated nectar is found in members of the Ranunculaceae, Berberidaceae and some Fabaceae. Glucose and fructose dominated nectars are found in representatives of the Brassicaceae, Apiaceae and some Asteraceae. Most Brassicaceae nectar contains no sucrose, and oil-seed rape nectars yield more glucose than fructose; dandelion is also high in glucose. Most of the nectars found in the Fabaceae contain equal quantities of all three sugars, although red clover and false-acacia nectars produce more fructose than glucose.

Within individual flowers of several of the Brassicaceae (rape, turnip, sweet alison, garden radish, charlock, thale cress), nectar is produced from both the lateral nectaries (associated with the short stamens) and the median nectaries (outside the long stamens). On average 95% of the total nectar carbohydrate is produced from the lateral nectaries and this nectar has a higher glucose:fructose ratio (usually 1.0 : 1.2) compared with that from the median nectaries (0.2 : 0.9). Anatomical studies of these brassica flowers show that the lateral nectary glands are supplied with relatively rich amounts of phloem tissue (food-conducting), whilst the supply to the median glands is poor.

Sugar concentration is highly dependent on the anatomy of the vascular system that supplies the nectary. Highly concentrated nectar is characteristic of several plant species where the nectar originates from phloem tissue as demonstrated in the anatomical studies of the brassica flowers described above. Plants that produce high volumes of dilute nectar have limited connection to phloem tissue, but a greater degree of connection with xylem (water-conducting) tissue.

Controlled experiments with honey bees have shown that nectars containing sucrose, glucose, and fructose in the same ratios are the most attractive to them. However in nature, the usual ratio in flower nectar actually used by bees is 2:1:1. An equal mix is less common.

Some of the more important carbohydrates found in nectar and honeydew, and their value or otherwise to bees are described in the following table.

TABLE 3 TYPES OF SUGARS AND THEIR IMPORTANCE TO HONEY BEES

TYPE OF CARBOHYDRATE	TYPE OF SUGAR	IMPORTANT PROPERTIES
Monosaccharides (70% of honey by weight)	Glucose (dextrose)	Energy
	Fructose (laevulose)	Energy
	Galactose	Inedible to the honey bee
Disaccharides	Sucrose	Broken down by invertase to glucose and fructose
	Maltose	Secondary sugar resulting from breakdown of sucrose
	Trehalose	Not important as a blood sugar in honey bees c.f. other insects
Trisaccharides (in the case of melezitose 0.3% of nectar honey and up to 8% honeydew honey)	Melezitose Raffinose	Found in honeydew, bee has difficulty breaking down melezitose and raffinose

Nectar production in flowers has received comparatively little attention from crop breeders, agronomists, and horticulturalists. It is a subject that should not be overlooked, because where pollinating insects are a scarce resource, crop plants will be competing with other plant species for the attention of pollinating insects, especially if these plants are producing nectar, either with a higher sugar concentration in greater quantity, or more pollen than the crop.

CONVERSION OF NECTAR TO HONEY

There are two main processes involved in the conversion of nectar to honey:

- The conversion of the disaccharide sugar sucrose to the monosaccharide sugars glucose and fructose (a chemical process).
- The increased concentration of sugars in the nectar due to the evaporation of water (a physical process).

In the chemical process the worker bees add the enzyme invertase secreted from their hypopharyngeal glands whilst returning from their foraging activities; this converts the sucrose present in the nectar to fructose and glucose. In the hive the nectar is transferred from the forager to a receiver bee that ingests and swallows it. The conversion process continues as the receiver bee regurgitates a small drop of the nectar into the fold of her partly extended proboscis (the sucking apparatus of the mouthparts). By repeatedly exposing it to the air, the moisture content of the nectar droplet is reduced; she will do this 80-90 times over a period of 20 minutes on the same droplet of nectar. She then hangs it up in the comb and starts the whole process again on a new droplet of nectar. The worker bees create currents of air to draw dry air across the comb and displace the moist warm air around the cells. This completes the process of reducing the moisture content of the nectar down to around 20%.

NECTAR CONSUMPTION BY THE COLONY

Each year a colony requires around 120 kg of nectar. Approximately 70 kg is consumed during the summer months to provide food for the brood and the adults, for their own nutrition, for extra energy to keep the broodnest warm (35-36°C) and to provide energy for foraging. The balance of nectar is converted to around 20 kg of honey that is stored in the colony and consumed during the cold flowerless months.

A colony's heat production in mid winter is of the order of 40 watts, which is enough to keep the surface bees from falling from the cluster and dying even when the temperatures outside are −30°C or below. Such intense heat production consumes a lot of energy and a colony will use nearly a kg of honey per week throughout the winter months (Seeley 1995).

INFLUENCE OF TYPES OF NECTAR ON HONEY GRANULATION, FERMENTATION AND STORAGE

HONEY GRANULATION

Honey granulates because it is a supersaturated solution containing more sugars than can normally remain in solution. The supersaturated solution is unstable, and in time can only return to the stable state by some of the sugars being thrown out of solution i.e. they granulate. Glucose is less soluble in water than fructose and this property has an important bearing on the granulation of honey. A high glucose:fructose ratio in the nectar will produce a rapid granulation, however it is the glucose : water ratio that is more closely related to the granulation tendency of the honey. Honey with a ratio of 1 water :1.7 glucose or lower will not granulate; whereas a ratio of 1 water : 2.1 glucose or higher usually means there will be rapid granulation. The optimum granulation temperature for honey is 13-15°C. The sugar crystals in the granulated honey melt between 36 - 39°C. Granulation can be promoted by the presence of minute crystals, air bubbles, particles of wax, pollen grains and dust, both in honey stores in the hive and in honey after extraction from the comb.

HONEY FERMENTATION

The moisture content of the honey is important because if it is between 17% and 20%, in the presence of osmophilic yeasts (active between 10 and 20°C), there is a risk the honey will ferment and the glucose and fructose will be metabolised to produce alcohol and water. Above 22% moisture content there is an increased risk of fermentation, even if osmophilic yeasts are absent.

When honey granulates there is increased water content between the sugar crystals allowing the osmophilic yeasts to become active. Some of the wild yeasts found in flowers and in soil are osmophilic. Non-granulated honey will also ferment if the moisture content and yeast count are the same as those found in fermenting granulated honey.

Storing honey at less than 10°C discourages granulation and fermentation, but if stored at more than 27°C it will be damaged and this can be detected by measuring the increased content of hydroxymethylfurfuraldehyde (HMF) and the reduced diastase level. As well as the effect on the taste and value of the honey, there is a statutory level of HMF in the UK above which honey should not be sold (not above 40 ppm).

STORAGE OF HONEY

Honey should be stored in airtight containers in as dry an atmosphere as possible, preferably around 12°C in order to ensure a good shelf life, and no loss of taste and flavour.

NECTAR

Pollen

WHY STUDY POLLEN?

The majority of insect-pollinated plants have pollen that is nutritious to bees, and so it is important to understand its nutritive value. Knowledge about pollen also enables the beekeeper to know which plant species the worker honey bee has visited when collecting her pollen load. In melissopalynology, the study of pollen grains in honey, pollen identification is essential for determining the geographical and botanical origin of honey. Such studies are crucial in deciding if claims made regarding the origin of a sample of honey are fraudulent.

Rex Sawyer's books, 'Honey Identification' and 'Pollen Identification for Beekeepers', are good introductory texts.

THE DEVELOPMENT AND FUNCTION OF POLLEN

Pollen is produced by the male sex organs of the plant and contains the male gametes. It originates from pollen mother cells in the anther. The pollen mother cells divide by meiosis to produce four immature pollen grains. The nuclei of each of these then divides by mitosis to produce a cell containing two nuclei, one of which will control the development of the pollen tube, the other, the generative nucleus, will divide again to form two male gametes. After anther dehiscence, a pollen grain containing the male gametes is transferred to a receptive stigmatic surface upon which it germinates.

MICROSCOPY

Pollen grains are very small, ranging from 5-140 microns in diameter (5 microns in forget-me-not to 140 microns in hollyhocks), on average 20-30 microns; and the electron microscope has been used in the study of pollen grains enabling a much more detailed understanding of their structure to be achieved. However, for the routine examination and identification of pollen samples obtained by beekeepers, food scientists, and students, the high powered light microscope is adequate enough to enable them to scan prepared slides to get a quantitative estimate of the different species represented in samples taken.

With light microscopy, the techniques required to prepare the slides are relatively simple, enabling a large number of different grains to be examined both in sectional and surface view easily and quickly, usually at x 400 magnification.

Examination of pollen grains under the microscope enables the viewer to build up a mental, three-dimensional picture and to use the diagnostic characteristics of the plant species to determine the pollen present in the sample.

In order to study them and identify their source a number of methods can be used:

• Preparing slides from pollen loads collected from bees.
• Preparing slides of pollen collected directly from flowers.
• Techniques for preparing samples to examine pollen in honey using centrifugation or sedimentation.

Annex II lists methods that can be used for preparing slides of pollen grains.

POLLEN STRUCTURE

Pollen grains may be round, triangular, oblong, or boat-shaped. They are living cells surrounded by protective coats, namely the intine and exine. The very outer surface is sometimes called the sexine. It is made of sporopollenin, a complex polymer that is one of the most resistant natural materials known. Simple pollen grains consist of one cell only, whilst compound grains are several grains united. These may be in groups of four, called pollen tetrads as are found in members of the Ericaceae.

Within the outer layers of the protective coats are features that look like, and are known as bases, rods, or columns, and a roof or tectum. The outer surface may also have characteristic features; it may be smooth, granular, coarse or pitted, have spines, ridges, projections or a net-like appearance (reticulate). Apertures may be present, either in the shapes of furrows, known as colpi or as round or oval pores. The presence or absence of these features varies from one plant family or species to another, and as such are used diagnostically although sometimes they are not sufficiently different to identify to the species or even family level (fig. 23, page 45).

POLLEN COMPOSITION

The composition of pollen varies according to the plant source, and the following types of substances have been identified in pollen samples.

• Lipids (essential for the production of brood food).
• Carbohydrates and related compounds such as cellulose and lignin.

Table 4 CHARACTERISTICS OF POLLEN GRAINS FROM SOME IMPORTANT BEE PLANTS

Common name	Family	Botanical name	Pollen size microns	Shape	No. of pores / furrows	Surface texture
Apple	Rosaceae	*Malus spp.*	35	Rounded	3	Smooth
Field bean	Fabaceae	*Vicia faba*	35–40	Long oval elongated	3	Smooth
Oil-seed rape	Brassiceae	*Brassica napus*	c. 35	Round / irregular round	3	Net or pitted
Dandelion	Asteraceae	*Taraxacum officinalis*	c. 30	Multi–sided / irregular	3	Spines and other projections
Borage	Boraginaceae	*Borago officinalis*	c. 30	Round / irregular round	10	Indefinite/irregular
Heather (Ling)	Ericaceae	*Calluna vulgaris*	c. 45	Tetrad	3	Smooth
Hazel	Betulaceae	*Corylus avellana*	25	Oval / flat / triangular	3	Smooth
Forget-me-not	Boraginaceae	*Myosotis spp.*	c. 6	Dumbbell	10	Smooth
Crocus	Iridaceae	*Crocus aureus*	c. 100	Round	Slits	Granular
Hawthorn	Rosaceae	*Crataegus monogyna*	c. 40	Triangular	3	Striated

- Major minerals including potassium, sodium, calcium, and magnesium.
- Organic acids including phenolic acids.
- Free amino acids (main source of nitrogen for bees).
- Nucleic acids, DNA, RNA.
- Terpenes.
- Enzymes.
- Vitamins, including B2 (riboflavin), B6 (niacin), pantothenic acid, biotin, C (ascorbic acid) and E.
- Nucleosides.
- Pigments, carotenoids, and flavonoids.
- Plant growth regulators.

Depending on their plant source, pollens have a protein content that varies from 2-28%, expressed as crude protein from air-dried samples. Pollen is almost the only source of protein naturally available to bees, as the normal protein content of nectar is very low, one of the highest being found in ling heather that contains up to 1.5% protein and up to 2% in the honey.

HOW BEES USE POLLEN

Protein is essential for adequate fat cell development in fat bodies. Fat, glycogen, protein, and albumin are stored in the fat bodies that are located along the inside of the dorsal part of the abdomen. Pollen also contains up to 5% lipids, these are important as bees cannot synthesise cholesterol without the essential sterol precursors obtained from pollen. Bees that must over winter in the colony are physiologically different from summer bees, and must develop good fat bodies to enable them to survive the winter, and be able to sustain the provision of brood food during the early part of the season, when pollen sources are scarce, or bad weather prevents foraging. In August / early September, the adult worker bees and the newly developing bees feed very heavily upon pollen; this brings their hypopharyngeal glands back into the plump condition of the young nursing bee to enable them to feed the brood in spring. The amount of pollen required to rear a single worker has been estimated at between 125-145mg, and on average this contains about 30 mg of protein. The importance of a continual supply of pollen throughout the beekeeping season is the most important factor in whether or not a particular apiary location will support healthy and productive colonies. During the summer a colony rears approximately 150,000 bees, and therefore the quantity of pollen required to be collected is around 20kg. However, colony requirements vary and figures ranging from 15 –55 kg have been recorded.

Pollen is essential for young bees in the first 5-6 days after emergence to ensure their hypopharyngeal glands develop, and later in the secretion of wax during the comb-building phase of their lives (12-18 days after emergence as adults). Hypopharyngeal gland development is necessary for young adult

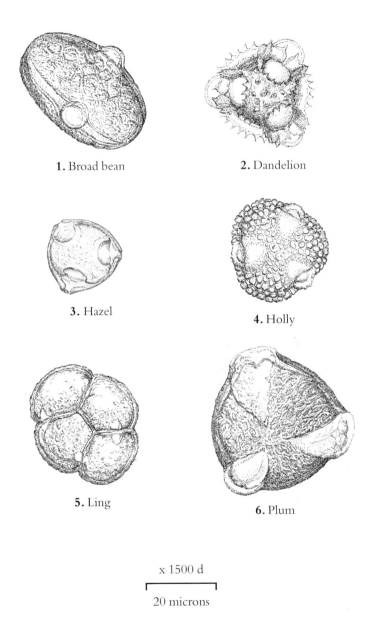

1. Broad bean

2. Dandelion

3. Hazel

4. Holly

5. Ling

6. Plum

x 1500 d

20 microns

Figure 23. Drawings of magnified pollen grains
of some important bee plants.
(After Hodges 1984)

worker bees to produce the special brood food to feed the brood.

Many pollen sources are also rich in oil and wax-soluble substances, usually yellow or orange in colour; dandelion pollen is a good example. The importance of the other compounds found in pollen is poorly understood and further research is necessary.

POLLEN LOAD COLOUR

Hodges' classic work, 'The Pollen Loads of the Honeybee', and the more recent 'Colour Guide to the Pollen Loads of the Honeybee' by Kirk, describe the colours of pollen loads. Hodges recorded the pollen load colours using matching watercolour paints, whilst Kirk used CMYK screen tint percentages, as used by printers, for the four-colour printing process. CMYK stands for cyan, magenta, yellow and the key plate, the plate that carries the black. CMYK is a subtractive model whereby the colours are removed by degrees to provide the required hue. As well as being an enjoyable experience there is much information to be gained from observing the pollen loads being brought back to the colony. Bees returning with full pollen baskets are a good indication that young brood is being reared and that the colony is queen-right.

It is often possible to identify the sources of pollen being worked from the colour of the pollen loads. These show considerable variation and these differences can largely be accounted for by:
- The human individual's perception of colour.
- It may have already been moistened with nectar / honey by the time it is viewed.
- Physical manipulation by bees.
- The lighting conditions in which it is viewed.

Despite these considerations, it is often possible though a combination of the pollen load colour, the flowering time, and knowledge of the local plants, to narrow down the identification to a choice of one or two species.

Kirk recommends that to identify a pollen load you should:
- Find a place in bright indirect sunlight.
- Ensure the light is not affected by factors such as reflections off coloured walls, light shining through leaves, or colours at sunset.
- Sit with your back to the light from windows when indoors.
- Let the light fall from behind you onto the pollen chart with the pollen load held on the end of a long pin.
- Hold the pollen load over the colour chart and match it, tilting the chart to avoid reflection off the surface of the paper.

Pollens from most species are shades of yellow or orange, some of the obvious exceptions are shown in Table 5.

Table 5 EXAMPLES OF PLANTS WITH
DISTINCTIVE POLLEN COLOURS

Near Black / purplish	field poppy	June-July
Deep Blue	scilla	Mar-Apr
Brick-red	horse-chestnut	May-June
Pale blue	rosebay willowherb	July-Aug
White	bluebell	Apr-June
Off-white	balsam	Aug-Sept

POLLEN PROCESSING AND STORAGE

On her return to the hive the forager bearing pollen enters the hive to deposit her pollen. Often she inspects a number of cells before selecting one that is satisfactory, usually located just above or beside the brood nest so it is readily available to the nurse bees, the younger hive bees, and those carrying out the rest of the pollen processing. The processor bees tamp the pollen down tightly to exclude air and incorporate with it a little regurgitated honey that inhibits the germination of pollen grains and bacterial growth. Germination inhibition is due to the presence of a phytocidal acid that is related to 10-hydroxy-2-decenoic acid (10-HDA) secreted by the hypopharyngeal and/or mandibular glands. Inhibition of bacterial growth is due to hydrogen peroxide generated by glucose oxidase secreted by the worker's hypopharyngeal glands. Enzymes are also added to the pollen during manipulation, and these promote initial digestion and prevent anaerobic metabolism and fermentation. The pollen can then be kept until required by the colony and in this condition it is often called 'bee bread'.

REGULATION OF POLLEN COLLECTION BY THE COLONY

Most of the pollen consumption takes place during the spring and summer months when brood rearing is most intense. The intake of pollen by a colony undergoes far greater fluctuations than does its demand. To manage this balance a colony builds a stockpile of approximately 1 kg and this will last at least a week, usually sufficient to buffer the colony and keep it nourished in the event of a failure in the external pollen supply, or during a period of bad weather. A shortage of pollen significantly reduces the amount of brood reared and thus fewer worker bees emerging 2–3 weeks after the pollen shortage.

A colony adjusts its collecting rate with respect to the pollen reserve partly through changes in the total number of active pollen foragers, and partly through changes in the per capita collecting rate. The mechanism whereby the pollen foragers obtain information on their colony's pollen reserves is probably through excitatory feedback in the case of too little pollen in the hive, which causes the nurse bees to prepare more cells for pollen storage. As a result the returning forager bees have more space to unload their pollen. Foraging behaviour is further discussed later (page 71).

POLLEN AND ITS EFFECT ON THE GROWTH OF LARVAE AND ADULTS

The complete food requirements of worker larvae have not been precisely determined, and no artificial diet has been found to replace the honey, pollen, and glandular secretions fed to the larvae. During days 1 and 2 of the worker larva's life the nurse bees feed brood food; a mixture of mandibular and hypopharyngeal gland secretions. On or around day 3 the amount of brood food is reduced, and honey and pollen is added to the diet with the peak of pollen feeding on day 5.

Queen larvae are fed a different diet compared to worker and drone larvae. It is a more concentrated food with a different composition called royal jelly. One of the key differences is the higher amount of sugars in the royal jelly fed to the queen larvae, which act as a phagostimulant to increase their appetites. Queen larvae are also mass-provisioned in their cells, so have access to food after the cell is capped on day 9. A larva up to 3 days old can become either queen, or worker, and this different feeding regime results in a series of physiological processes that produce a queen.

During the first 3-10 days after emergence the young adult workers need pollen for complete post-emergence glandular development and the growth of internal structures. During this period, their hypopharyngeal and mandibular glands are used to produce brood food to be fed to developing larvae. After that, pollen is not essential unless the older worker has to restart producing brood food and feeding larvae, because colony circumstances require it.

Worker bees that are raised in the autumn have little or no brood to feed, and they live for six or more months through the winter before starting their brood food production early in spring, after which they are replaced by spring reared worker bees. Drone larvae are fed more than worker larvae with brood food that contains a greater range of proteins. The production of spermatozoa is not dependent on the amount of protein fed to young drones, but brood food and pollen feeding may have an influence on drone longevity and mating ability. Young drones beg food from young workers, and are fed a mixture of brood food, pollen, and honey. Older drones feed themselves exclusively from honey taken from the comb, and this provides the energy for mating flights.

PRESENTATION AND DEHISCENCE OF POLLEN

Flowers can be described either as 'protected,' or 'open' and therefore exposed to the weather. The disadvantage of open flowers is that the flower organs may be readily damaged by frost, rain, or wind, and pollen may become damp; it needs to be kept dry to enable effective transference by bees. As a protection against this open flowers will only expand in sunshine and will remain closed during dull or wet weather, although some open flowers cannot actually close, e.g. plum. Damage to the flowers, or a lack of pollinating insects at the time of flowering in early spring, results in wide variations of plum crops from year to year. The snowdrop is an open flower, but in bad weather it actively droops so that the perianth protects the flower organs from damage. In tubular and bell shaped flowers the flower organs are always well protected from the weather, and remain accessible to the pollinating insect all of the time.

In order that the pollen grains can be liberated to bring about pollination the anthers dehisce when they are positioned for dehiscence, this is called presentation. In most species dehiscence takes place through a longitudinal split that appears between each pair of pollen sacs in each anther lobe. The split gradually enlarges by the separation and curling back of the walls of the anther lobes to produce a cavity into which pollen grains are released. If the cavity faces towards the centre of the flower the dehiscence is said to be introrse, if towards the outside, extrorse, and if sideways, lateral. Sometimes, as in the case of the Ericaceae, the dehiscence is through pores in the anthers, and is said to be poricidal.

In the northern hemisphere pollen dehiscence in open flowers usually takes place between 7am and 5pm, but the peak of pollen presentation and dehiscence varies between species as does the duration of dehiscence. For example, a single flower in one species may produce pollen over many days, whilst another species may produce pollen for a single day. In the case of the hellebore, dehiscence in individual flowers may last up to 26 days, whilst individual florets on the head of the dandelion may present all their day's quota of pollen within 10 minutes of the capitulum opening. In the cabbage, dehiscence of all the anthers takes place at once, whilst in other crucifers the period may be typically 1-2 hours. In the dwarf cherry, dehiscence of all the anthers in one flower takes place in 1-2 days, in the strawberry 1-3 days, and the blackberry in 1-4 days.

Local environmental factors such as temperature, dull or sunny weather influence anther dehiscence. Dandelion requires an air temperature of at least 10°C in dull weather; dehiscence in apple will occur as low as 1°C. Hellebores, horse-chestnut, pear, and cherry laurel dehisce throughout the day and night.

Table 6 THE EFFECTS OF AIR TEMPERATURE AND LIGHT DENSITY ON ANTHER DEHISCENCE

	AIR TEMPERATURE IN DULL WEATHER °C	AIR TEMPERATURE IN SUNNY WEATHER °C
Scilla siberica	4.7	8.5
Snowdrop	5.0	9.0
Crocus	4.0	9.4

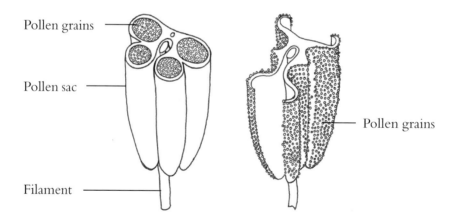

Figure 24. Undehisced anther with top removed to show sacs containing pollen grains and a dehisced anther

The time of dehiscence for some bee plants can be grouped as follows:

- Early morning – poppy, charlock, traveller's joy.
- Mainly morning – dandelion, wood anemone, aubretia, gorse.
- Midday – crocus.
- Mainly afternoon – apple, pear.
- Afternoon – broad bean.
- All day – wallflower, bramble, phacelia.

THE POLLEN CYCLE

Beekeepers call the availability of pollen during the year, the pollen cycle, and it is of crucial importance in determining the type of beekeeping that the area can sustain. The pollen cycle varies in different locations, and usually starts in the early spring with plants such as crocus, willow, snowdrop, and aconite, followed by top fruit, dandelion, hawthorn, horse-chestnut, and other spring and summer flowers. In mid-summer these are followed by clovers and lime, and rosebay willowherb and brambles are important in late summer. The pollen cycle is complete with heathers, thistles, ivy, and balsam where it occurs.

Honeydew and Propolis

WHAT IS HONEYDEW?

Honeydew should not be confused with nectar. Nectar is actively secreted by nectaries, whereas honeydew requires the intermediary stage of a sap-sucking insect. Honeydew also differs in composition from nectar in that it contains enzymes derived from the gut and saliva of the intermediary insect. Some types contain the sugar melezitose, which is so insoluble in water that it crystallises on the surface of the plant.

Honeydew is produced through the activities of plant-sucking insects (Hemiptera) these include aphids and scale insects. These insects have mouthparts that are modified to pierce into the tissues of the host plant and feed on the sap inside the plant's phloem tissue. The sap comes out from the injected hole due to the internal pressure in the plant's vascular system, and the action of the insect sucking, speeds up the process. The ingested sap passes into the gut of the insect and, after digestion, it is excreted as droplets of honeydew. These droplets are collected by a number of insects including honey bees. Honeydew may be produced in significant quantities in certain seasons when the weather is hot and dry favouring the build-up of populations of sap-sucking insects.

PLANT SOURCES

In the British Isles trees are the most important source of the honeydew that is exploited by honey bees. Species such as beech, oak, poplar, scots pine, and larch only produce honeydew, whilst trees such as sycamore, small and large-leaved limes, and sweet chestnut will yield both nectar and honeydew. Whilst not worked by bees, honeydew can also be seen on the leaves of stinging nettles on warm summer nights and is exploited by moths.

COMPOSITION OF HONEYDEW HONEY

Honeydew honey contains catalases, amylase, and acid phosphatase; enzymes derived from the plant, together with peptidase and proteinase enzymes from the sap-sucking insect. It usually contains significant amounts of the trisaccharide sugars melezitose, erlose and raffinose, and dextran, a polyglucose.

The amounts of glucose and fructose in honeydew honey are usually less than in honey produced from plant nectar. Honeydew honey is characterised by the presence of algae and sooty moulds as well as dust and soot particles. The presence of these materials can affect the colour, the flavour, and the keeping qualities of the honey.

USE BY BEES AS FOOD

Honeydew honey is considered to be unsuitable for feeding over-wintering bees because it may have a high protein content that can cause a dysenteric condition when bad weather prevents them from flying frequently to void faecal matter. However, most honeydew honeys are considered safe for the colony to use to build-up in the spring.

WHAT IS PROPOLIS?

Propolis consists of naturally occurring materials that honey and other bees collect from living plants and use alone or with beeswax in the construction and adaptation of their nests. It is a resinous substance varying in colour from light tan to black. It is heavier than water and water repellent. It is sticky at hive temperatures around 35°C, becoming quite hard below 15°C and brittle below 5°C. The composition of propolis depends upon its source and the time of year, but typically it contains:

- 55% – balsams, resins, flavonoids, phenolic esters and acids.
- 30% – waxes.
- 10% – ethereal oils.
- 5% – pollen.
- <5% – fatty acids, essential oils and other organic chemicals and minerals.

SOURCES OF PROPOLIS

Propolis is collected from a large variety of trees, shrubs, and plants, especially from the leaf buds of poplar trees. Other examples include sunflowers, birch, alder, beech, willows, horse-chestnut, plum, and cherry. It is usually collected during very warm weather when the resins are soft enough for the bees to manipulate. Propolis collection is a specialist task, and a worker will not collect propolis at the same time as pollen or nectar. After collection it is carried back to the colony in globules on the pollen collecting apparatus of the bee's hind leg, and deposited in the places where it is required.

USE BY BEES

Bees use propolis to seal up holes and gaps in hives or the natural cavities in which they live. It is used to coat the internal surfaces of the woodwork of a conventional beehive like a varnish, to strengthen the comb structure, and as an antiseptic lining in the cells to protect them from moulds and other infections.

It is also used in the mummification of unwanted objects such as dead mice that are too big to move from the colony, thus preventing them from decomposing.

Adaptations

INTERDEPENDENCE

Flowers need to be pollinated, and bees need the raw materials of nectar and pollen, and as a consequence the process of evolutionary pressure has resulted in adaptations to the mutual benefit of plants and bees. This chapter discusses some of them.

Most flowering plants need to attract pollinators in order to transfer their pollen from one plant to fertilise the ovules of another of the same species. Such pollinators include honey bees and they are rewarded by the presence of pollen and/or nectar, both of which are essential for honey bee survival.

Flowers exhibit a wide range of structure and flowering characteristics, the purposes of which are not fully understood. It is possible that the pollinators themselves may have adapted to flowering patterns caused by other environmental factors; conversely the flowering rhythms may have been selected under evolutionary pressure to suit the foraging behaviour of the pollinator.

Flowering plants have developed many different strategies to exploit insects, birds, bats, and other animals, to effect the transfer of pollen from plant to plant. Some flowering plants have flowers that can be pollinated by a range of species, whilst others may be highly specialised and utilise only one species.

Bees require nectar as an immediate energy source and as the raw material for producing honey that can be stored for use when there is no nectar available. They also need pollen, their principal source of protein, for building body tissues, and propolis for its antiseptic and mechanical properties. Flowering plants are the main source of these materials.

REWARDS

Flowers can be categorised by the food reward they offer the honey bee. Nectar flowers reward nectar and pollen, e.g. red and white clover, and blackberry; others are nectarless, but produce abundant pollen, e.g. poppies and gorse. Nectar flowers can be further divided into those flowers where the nectar is freely exposed so that short or long-tongued insects can reach it, including honey bees; others have the nectar available at the bottom of a corolla tube and thus only long-tongued insects can reach it.

FLOWERS SUPPLY AND BEES COLLECT

Bees have different strategies for tackling different kinds of flower shapes to gain access to the nectar and pollen. In the case of open flowers a visiting bee bites the anthers and uses her forelegs to pull them towards her, thus liberating the pollen, e.g. bramble and raspberries. For tubular flowers she inserts her proboscis for nectar, and pollen is incidentally caught on her legs and mouthparts, e.g. disc florets in dandelion, also ling heather. Where the flowers are closed, e.g. in some members of the Fabaceae, she may gain access to the nectar by biting the base of the flower and inserting her proboscis. This leaves a small hole allowing access to the nectar for other insects and sometimes results in pollination failure, especially if the flower is self-incompatible.

In some flowers, e.g. broad bean, the honey bee exploits a hole already cut into the base of the flower by a bumblebee, usually *Bombus terrestris*, that also has a relatively short tongue. Other plants where this occurs include red clover, monk's-hood, comfrey, snapdragon, and penstemon. Many species of the Lamiaceae family have a hard, ribbed, often bristly or even spiny calyx that prevents bees biting into the base of the flower.

Where the flower is a spike or catkin the forager runs up and down it causing the pollen to be shaken onto her body hairs, e.g. hazel. In some flowers the bee's abdomen is pressed against the flower, pushing the pollen mass outside it and onto her body and these are called presentation flowers, e.g. claries.

Certain flower shapes or forms attract bees, e.g. a flower with a long outline in relation to the overall flower size. A flower shape that is divided into 5 separated petals is more attractive to honey bees than a fused circle. Flower parts are arranged so that the bee scrabbles about gathering pollen or nectar and in the process becomes dusted with pollen grains that then become transferred to the next flower she visits.

Flowers of the Lamiaceae have a two-lipped corolla, the lower lip of which is modified to form a platform on which the bee alights. The stamens are located under the shelter of the upper lip of the corolla, so that when the bee enters the flower for nectar, pollen is transferred onto her back; these are called nototribic flowers, e.g. white dead-nettle (fig. 25, page 59). Other flowers deposit pollen on the underside of the bee. In this case the stamens and style are often housed within a keel-shaped lower lobe that is easily pushed down by a slight pressure from above by the insect landing on the keel; this exposes the style and the anthers and allows access to the nectary. These are sternotribic flowers typically found in the Fabaceae, e.g. sweet pea (fig. 26, page 59).

Some plants are even more modified, for example salvia, where in order to

Stigma brushes bee's back   Anther

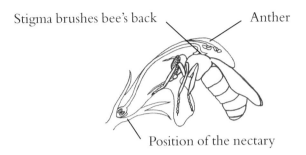

Position of the nectary

Figure 25. White dead-nettle *(Lamium album)* showing nototribic
pollination where pollen is dusted/picked up on the bee's back

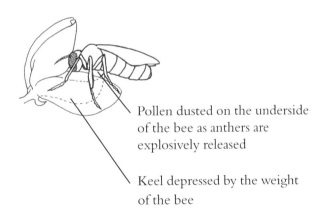

Pollen dusted on the underside
of the bee as anthers are
explosively released

Keel depressed by the weight
of the bee

Figure 26. Sweet Pea *(Lathyrus odoratus)*, a typical sternotribic flower where
pollen is dusted/picked up on the underside of the bee.

gain access to the nectary at the base of the ovary, the bee must push past a barrier formed by the lower parts of two stamens. Here there are two perfect (fertile) stamens, each has a pair of branches, the upper and longer carrying an anther, the lower branch bearing an atrophied anther called a staminode. The two aborted anthers are united by a connective. When the bee enters the flower she pushes against the connective and this moves the staminodes that then lever the upper branch of the stamen forward so the fertile anthers are pressed firmly onto her back. Salvia flowers are protandrous and later in the flowering process the long, fully arched style lengthens and bends down so that its forked tip, bearing the stigma, blocks the entrance to the corolla, thus filling the position formerly occupied by the depressed anthers. When a bee, searching for nectar, visits the flower at its female stage she finds her way barred by the forked tip of the style. The visiting bee bringing pollen from another flower pushes past the style to gain access to the nectary, brushing pollen on the now receptive stigma, thus ensuring cross-pollination.

In some other members of the Lamiaceae there is no hindrance to bees probing in the corolla, but there may be limitations on the types of bee that can exploit the nectar depending on the length of the corolla and the length of the bee's tongue. The honey bee's proboscis length is approximately 6 mm, but if the nectar rises in the corolla tube high enough for the bee's proboscis to contact the meniscus, all of it can be sucked up. Other members of the Lamiaceae have shorter corolla tubes, thus their nectar is easily accessible to the honey bee, e.g. small flowered mints, thymes, lavender, rosemary, and cat-mint, these are all favourite honey bee plants.

BEE ADAPTATIONS

In order to work flowers to obtain pollen and nectar bees have specialised structures and behaviour mechanisms. These are described in the following pages.

MOUTHPARTS

The mouthparts of the worker honey bee are required to perform a range of tasks including grasping and manipulation; the collection of pollen and its ingestion; the collection of nectar from flowers, propolis, honeydew, and water for the dilution of stored honey, and colony humidity control. In addition the mouthparts are used to manipulate wax in the production of new wax comb and cappings.

The true mouthparts comprise the mandibles, maxillae, and the labium. The proboscis is an elongated tongue for lapping up liquids, surrounded by a tubular food canal formed from extensions of the maxillae and labium up which liquids are drawn by the pumping action of the walls of the cibarium. At the tip of the proboscis is the flabellum, it is dipped into the nectar or water

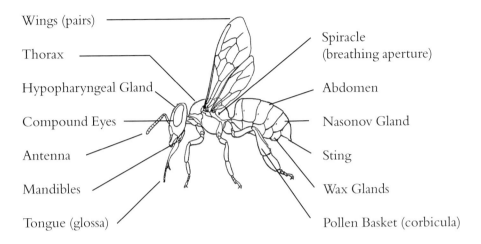

Wings (pairs)

Thorax

Hypopharyngeal Gland

Compound Eyes

Antenna

Mandibles

Tongue (glossa)

Spiracle
(breathing aperture)

Abdomen

Nasonov Gland

Sting

Wax Glands

Pollen Basket (corbicula)

Figure 27. Worker honey bee anatomy

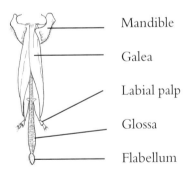

Mandible

Galea

Labial palp

Glossa

Flabellum

Figure 28. Mouthparts of the worker honey bee held in position by the
mandibles to form the proboscis for taking up nectar, water or honey

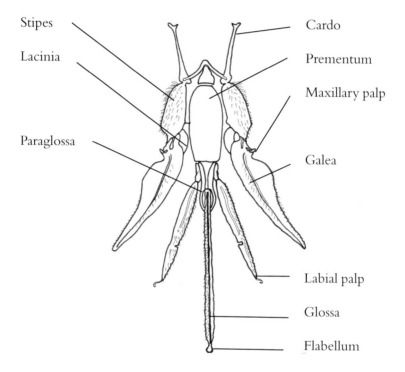

Stipes

Lacinia

Paraglossa

Cardo

Prementum

Maxillary palp

Galea

Labial palp

Glossa

Flabellum

Figure 29. Main parts of the worker honey bee proboscis expanded
(redrawn from Dade 1985).

enabling it to be collected. The proboscis, maxillae, and labium are held in position by the mandibles after they have been swung into place from under the bee's head. They are returned to their original position under the head when not in use.

The proboscis length is clearly important in terms of the flowers that different pollinating bees can visit. Some examples of average proboscis length in bees are given below:

Honey bees *Apis mellifera*

A. m. mellifera	(British Black)	5.7 – 6.4 mm
A. m. ligustica	(Italian)	6.3 – 6.6 mm
A. m. carnica	(Carniolan)	6.4 – 6.8 mm
A. m. caucasia	(Caucasian)	>6.5 mm

Solitary bees

Andrena spp. and Halictus spp.   2 – 7 mm

Bumblebees

Bombus lucorum	7.2 mm
B. praetorum	7.1 mm
B. lapidarius	8.1 mm
B. terrestris	8.2 mm
B. pascuorum	8.6 mm
B. hortorum	13.5 mm

Other bees

Anthophora spp.   15 – 21 mm

The structure of the mouthparts of honey bees has been well described and illustrated in Goodman (2003) and Davis (2004).

HAIRINESS AND COMBS

Bees are densely covered in branched or plumose hairs. Many of these are projections from sensory organs located within the bee's cuticle. The high degree of hairiness assists in the collection of pollen from the flowers visited, trapping pollen so that it can be recovered by the bee and packed together into a load. The loose pollen held on the bee's body is inadvertently transferred from one flower to another, promoting cross-pollination.

A flying bee builds up an electrostatic charge of at least 45 pC, equivalent to a potential of 450 volts on its body, this enables it to attract pollen. Most floral structures, including the anthers, are well insulated and pollen is attracted from the plant across an air gap of 0.5 mm. It is believed that the stigma is better

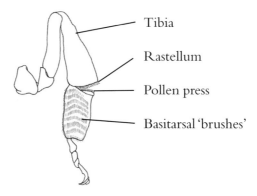

Tibia

Rastellum

Pollen press

Basitarsal 'brushes'

Figure 30. Inner surface of rear leg of worker honey bee to show
pollen brushes. (redrawn from Dade 1985).

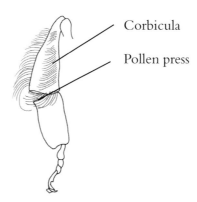

Corbicula

Pollen press

Figure 31. Outer surface of rear leg of worker honey bee to show retaining
hairs of the corbicula into which the pollen is packed
(redrawn from Dade 1985).

earthed than the other floral structures, so pollen on the incoming highly charged bees will be attracted preferentially to the stigma when they make contact with the flower.

Bees need to keep the sensory organs on their antennae free of pollen, and to achieve this the foreleg has an antennal notch containing fine hairs through which the antennae are drawn to comb the pollen grains onto the foreleg. The forelegs are also used to clean pollen from the front part of the body. The middle legs have rows of hairs on the basitarsii (lower part of the legs), and these are used to remove pollen from the forelegs and thorax. The hind legs have a wide angle of rotation, and bear rows of hairs that are used to comb the pollen from the middle legs and the thoracic region.

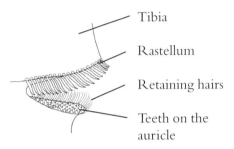

Tibia

Rastellum

Retaining hairs

Teeth on the auricle

Figure 32. Tibio-tarsal joint on rear worker leg showing the 'pollen press' (redrawn from Dade 1985)

The bee gathers pollen from all over her body and concentrates it by manipulation whilst in flight. She performs stereotyped grooming movements of the front and middle pairs of legs, and the pollen is combed backwards to the rear legs where it is compressed into the corbicula while the bee is still in flight, producing the familiar pollen loads seen on the rear legs of the worker honey bee. The corbicula, commonly referred to as the pollen basket, is formed on each hind leg from the slightly concave outer face of the tibia fringed by stiff hairs. It is not actually a basket, the pollen is held in place by hairs and bristles and physical compaction of the grains. The weight of a typical pollen load ranges from 10-30 mg.

FLOWER COLOUR AND BEE VISION

Bees need the ability to recognise the various features that characterise potential food source plants including flower colour, size, shape, symmetry, odour, height of the plant, and floral arrangement.

Flower parts contain a variety of chemicals called pigments, e.g. carotenoids that are yellow, red or brown in colour and anthocyanins, a major class of flavonoids that are responsible for most red, purple, and blue colours of flowers. Some flowers have a mixture of pigments.

Green foliage emits a weak, fairly uniform reflectance of ultra-violet (UV) light, and the blue and green areas of the spectrum; to the bee this appears as a greyish to a very weak bee-yellow. Blues, purple, reddish purple, yellows, and oranges are all common flower colours, and are within the range of colour vision of bees. Thus the brightly coloured petals offer a contrast to the green background that attracts the foraging bee. The spectral reflectance of flowers coincides with the greatest ability of bees for discriminating specific wavelengths of light. It is interesting to note that the colours of wild flowers relate to the colours their pollinators can see, whereas many cultivated varieties, developed to please the human eye, are less attractive to pollinators.

The visible spectrum of the bee's compound eye is in the range 300 to 650 nm (nanometers), in humans it is 370 to 750 nm. Bees have colour vision that is trichromatic like human colour vision, however unlike humans, their eyes are sensitive to UV light. Bee primary colours are ultra-violet, blue and yellow, which when mixed give bee-white. Bees can detect near UV light as a distinct colour that we refer to as bee-purple (actually a mixture of yellow and ultra-violet light) but we have no idea how it appears to them. Bees are red blind and see red as black, but some red flowers such as poppies contain pigments that reflect UV light, attracting bees and appearing to them as bee ultra-violet. The outer florets of the dandelion strongly reflect UV light, and the bee sees the dandelion flower as having a bee purple outer ring and a central disc of yellow. Yellow–blue, white-blue, red-white, and yellow-white are all recognisable colour contrasts for the bee's vision. The petals of forget-me-not flowers (not the corona) reflect in the blue region and therefore appear blue, referred to as bee-blue. Germander speedwell reflects UV light as well as blue and appears violet to the bee (referred to as bee-violet). Bees see blue, green, yellow, and orange much as we do.

In addition to perceiving colour the honey bee can also detect the directional nature of polarised light. Polarised light occurs where the electromagnetic vibrations of the light wave energy take place in the same plane. Bees are able to use the polarised part of the light spectrum that they perceive to determine the direction of the sun, enabling them to find their way back to the colony or to their foraging sites. There is usually sufficient light on cloudy days for the bees to receive enough polarised light to facilitate navigation.

Table 7 COMPARISON OF THE APPARENT PERCEPTION BY BEES
AND MAN OF DIFFERENT COLOURED FLOWERS

ACTUAL RANGE OF COLOUR(S) REFLECTED FROM THE FLOWER	COLOUR TO BEES	COLOUR TO MAN	EXAMPLE
Yellow	Yellow	Yellow	Cowslip
Green	Yellow	Green	*Helleborus foetidus*
Green+blue+red	Blue-green	White	Wild Cherry
Blue	Blue	Blue	Forget-me-not
Blue+red	Blue	Purple	Ling heather
Blue+UV	Violet	Blue	Germander speedwell
Blue +UV + red	Purple	Purple	Purple-loosestrife
UV + red	UV	Red	Field Poppy

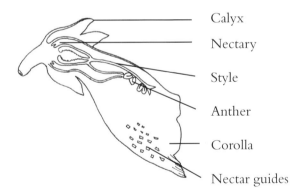

Figure 33. LS Foxglove *(Digitalis purpurea)* flower

NECTAR GUIDES

Nectar guides, found mainly on flower petals, may take the form of blotches, streaks or spots, either darker in colour than the rest of the petal or of a different and contrasting colour. Their purpose is to direct the pollinating bee to the location of the nectar, and thus come into contact with the anthers and stigmas. There are many examples of nectar guides, e.g. in horse-chestnut there is a yellow blotch on each of the lower petals. At first these are orange turning to pink as the flower ages. After successful pollination the nectar guides turn red, and the flowers become unattractive to bees and no longer secrete nectar. Other examples include spots or blotches in the foxglove, and clear lines in some species of geranium such as the pencilled crane's-bill that has magenta veins on almost white petals.

Many nectar guides utilise the ability of the bee to see UV light, e.g. meadow crane's-bill. The human eye sees them as faint lines radiating from the centre of the flower, whereas to the bee they appear as black lines on a pale background that reflects UV light.

BEES CAN SMELL AND TASTE

Bees have a hard exoskeleton through which the sensory organs must have access in order to function. Bees have olfactory (smell) receptors on the antennae that protrude forward from the body when the bee is in flight, so that volatile molecules contained in the air stream are drawn over them, stimulating the sensory cells. The olfactory sensory receptors contain large and small trichoid, coeloconic, and placoid sensillae. There are around 3000 trichoid sensillae on each worker antenna and around 2700 of the placoid sensillae.

Flower scent glands, usually situated on petals, produce volatile essential oils and other constituents belonging to many different groups of chemicals. In the horse chestnut the colour change described above is accompanied by a change in the scent that is perceived by bees, enabling them to distinguish between young and older flowers.

Bees have taste receptors in their mouths and mouthparts, antennae, on their feet, and on their genitalia; these are sensitive to sweet, salty, sour, acid, and bitter substances. Tasting in bees not only involves the sampling of potential food sources, but also the detection of pheromones, chemical substances released by the bees that influence the behaviour and the development of others in the colony.

The structure and the types of sensory organs and how they are located on the honey bee body are well illustrated in Goodman (2003) and Davis (2004).

FLOWERING TIMES AND BEE BEHAVIOUR

The time of flower opening is often directly related to the times when the pollinating insects are flying. Poppy flowers open between 5 and 6am, and have often completed their lives by midday. Virtually all the new flower buds of the broad bean open in the afternoon, more than 70% of them between 12 and 2pm. Many flowers have a definite opening and closing rhythm, e.g. dandelions open within 30 minutes of the sun's rays striking them, begin to close 3 hours later, and are shut within 5 hours of opening on a normal sunny day. Flowers that can open and close in this way are called chasmogamic; other examples are buttercups, roses, and poppies. In comparison cleistogamous flowers never open, and are self-pollinated, e.g. sweet violet. Some plants have a diurnal rhythm in which the petals open in the morning allowing bees to access the pollen and nectar, and close in the afternoon denying access. Tulips and crocuses show thermonasty, a response to a general, non-directional temperature stimulus; the crocus is sensitive to as little as 0.5°C change in temperature, and this change will determine the opening and closing of the flower. Pollen dehiscence is often periodic in nature.

Worker bees generally tend to 'prefer' nectar collection, but up to 25% of the foraging bees will collect pollen, and around 17% will collect both pollen and nectar. They also tend to specialise on one type of task at a time. Foraging bees will continue to work the plant species until pollen availability and/or the nectar flow ceases, or there is a superior source elsewhere. They will travel further for a pollen load as it weighs less and thus the journey consumes less energy. A typical pollen load weighs 10–30mg, whereas a nectar load is 25–40 mg.

Bees have a well-developed capacity to learn and remember geographical locations and sources of nectar and pollen, and to communicate this information through a range of behavioural devices called 'bee dances'.

ADAPTATIONS

Worker Honey Bee Foraging Behaviour

WORKER BEE LIFE CYCLE

It is perhaps not generally appreciated that when we see bees in the summer they are in the last phase of their life cycle. The worker honey bee goes through a series of activities during her life, although many of these activities are interdependent and adjust to the changing requirements and conditions, both within the colony, and in the external environment. During this she is engaged in a progressive change in behaviour and functions in the colony. The precise order and timing vary from individual to individual, and according to the needs of the colony. Sometimes the individual may revert to a previous activity if there is a requirement for it to be carried out, for example, after a colony has swarmed or suffered disease.

The schedule shown in Table 8 is for bees raised in the spring and summer when their lives are short because of the intense activity of brood rearing followed by foraging at the busiest time of the year. Pollen loads are usually

Table 8 THE SPRING AND SUMMER WORKER HONEY BEE LIFE CYCLE BASED ON DAYS AFTER EMERGENCE FROM THE CELL.

Days	Activities
0 – 6	Cell cleaning; general hive cleaning
3 – 10	Hypopharyngeal glands produce brood food; feeding the brood
3 – 15	Attending the queen cleaning and feeding her
6 – 18	Receiving and processing nectar
12 – 20	Wax glands fully developed; wax production and comb building
15 – 25	Flight muscles developing; hive ventilation
18 – 35	Venom gland and sting apparatus developed; colony guard duty
20 – Death	Flight muscles fully developed; bee attracted to light; foraging after short orientation flights; nectar and pollen collection
25 – Death	Water and propolis collection

collected more quickly than nectar, and load size tends to increase with increasing temperature. Nectar gatherers may make 5 - 8 trips per day, while pollen gatherers make 7 or more. They literally wear themselves out.

COMMUNICATION DANCES AND SIGNALS

Honey bees, as social insects, have evolved a highly developed ability to communicate with each other. This is used to exchange information about the status of forage sources and their qualities, and how to find them in a very effective and efficient way. However, although a bee can remember shapes and the appearance of objects she cannot communicate this information to other bees. The pioneer of the work on bee communication was Karl von Frisch and his students; their work is described in his book 'Dance Language and Orientation of Bees' published in 1967. Bee dances and their role in honey bee colonies have been well described in Winston (1987), Seeley (1995), and more recently in Schneider and Lewis (2003).

A number of dances are recognised, including the round dance, the waggle dance, and a dorso-ventral abdominal vibrating dance (DVAV), now more often called vibration signals. Other dances involving trembling, jostling, buzzing, and shaking have been described by researchers. Knowledge of the significance of these activities in honey bee colonies continues to increase as a result of research and observation. The round dance is the simplest dance and serves to inform other workers in the colony that there is a useful resource near to the colony, usually within 15 metres. The dance does not communicate the precise distance or the direction of the resource from the hive. In the round dance the worker bee makes small circles and every 2 –3 rotations she reverses and goes in the opposite direction. As she performs the dance she is closely followed and antennated (antennal contact made) by other worker bees.

The waggle dance communicates distance in terms of energy expenditure needed to reach the location, as well as direction and the quality of the forage at distances of more than 100 metres from the colony. This is achieved in its characteristic figure of eight, the number of waggles of the abdomen per vertical run across the comb face, and the direction of the runs on the comb in relation to the angle of the sun are interpreted by attendant worker bees which are recruited to forage (fig. 36, page 75). A food source 100 metres away from the colony is communicated by a waggle run lasting 1.35 seconds, whereas a food source located 4500 metres from the colony is shown by a waggle run of about 4 seconds.

Vibration signal behaviour is used to regulate the foraging and other activities of workers by enhancing the performance of many different tasks. For example, the vibration signal increases the likelihood of older bees to engage in foraging, whereas younger workers will respond by increasing the time they spend on tasks inside the nest, such as food processing and brood care. In performing the vibration signal behaviour a worker vibrates her body,

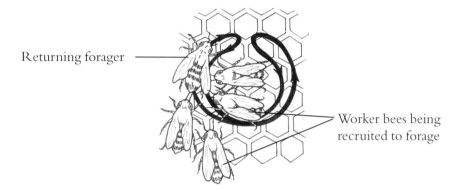

Returning forager

Worker bees being
recruited to forage

Figure 34. Round dance

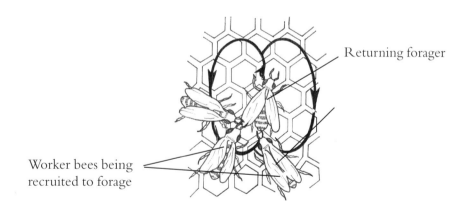

Returning forager

Worker bees being
recruited to forage

Figure 35. Waggle dance

particularly the abdomen, dorso-ventrally, using her legs to grasp another worker.

Tremble dances are performed by workers that are nectar foragers. These dances stimulate and recruit additional bees to function as receivers and food storers when the colony's rate of nectar collection has risen above its capacity for nectar processing. These dances also inhibit the production of waggle dances, and thus reduce the nectar collection rate, until a time when the rate is in balance with the colony's nectar processing capacity. In the tremble dance the worker holds her front legs in the air, whilst moving her body from side to side and up and down in a trembling movement. She then turns her body in a different, apparently random direction, and continues her trembling movement. The worker bee may continue this behaviour for more than an hour as she moves across large areas of the comb recruiting receiver bees.

FORAGING BEHAVIOUR AND OPTIMISING COLLECTING EFFICIENCY

Foraging behaviours are flexible and opportunistic in looking for new pollen and nectar sources, and when a good source of forage is found, bees may remain faithful to it for more than a day or so until it becomes depleted or less attractive. After this they will sample other sources and return to the original source only if it starts to be productive again. Bees searching for food are called scout bees, they are foraging bees that bring nectar and/or pollen back to the colony without having been stimulated and directed by dances performed by other foragers. It has been estimated that between 5 - 35% of the foraging bees in the colony perform this scout duty at any one time. Scout bees tend to be the more experienced foragers, and the proportion of scout bees in relation to the total foraging force depends on the availability of the nectar and pollen at that time. If forage is short, the proportion of scout bees increases thereby improving the chances of finding new resources. Differences in the forage due to chance discoveries by individual bees partly explains the differences in foraging behaviour of individual colonies in an apiary, where one colony may be exploiting a different forage source to its neighbour. This can be observed by the differences in pollen load colours being taken into different colonies in the apiary at the same time.

Research has shown that the majority of honey bee foragers do not find flowers themselves; they are directed there by means of the waggle dance carried out by other foragers acting as long distance scouts that are already working those flowers. The scout bee that finds a worthwhile resource returns to her colony and informs other worker bees of the location and worth of the resource through the waggle dance, recruiting them to go out and exploit it.

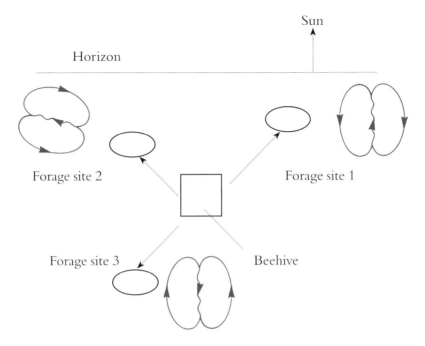

Figure 36. Waggle dances showing the orientation of the dance on the face of the comb in relation to the forage location and the sun.

The success of the foraging bees in their collection of pollen has a direct effect on the amount of brood that can be reared. Feeding the brood is a core activity for the nurse bees, and they adjust their brood rearing behaviour in relation to the amount of pollen stored in the brood combs. If an insufficient amount of pollen is being brought into the hive and pollen stores are depleted, the foraging bees will detect it as they inspect the comb when depositing their pollen load, and more workers will be recruited to forage for pollen.

Whilst bees prefer to forage near to the hive, it is known that they will forage for considerable distances away if the resource is sufficiently rewarding. Studies carried out by researchers at Sheffield University have shown that bees will forage to at least 10 km from their hives to visit heather moorland when the ling is secreting nectar (personal communication).

Bees are capable of choosing the better of two forage patches according to the rate at which they can collect nectar and pollen from them. A practical consequence of this is that honey bee colonies used for crop pollination should be placed at the edge or within the target crop. Bee visitation rates increase proportionately in flower patches that have increasing numbers of nectar-bearing flowers, nectar volume, and sugar concentration.

If the nectar output is relatively high, bees pollinate more efficiently because they will visit more flowers in a given period of time, and this is important when honey bees are being used to pollinate a crop. Having encountered a patch of profitable flowers, bees tend to forage in a straight line from the colony, and this has implications for the way hives are sited in crops.

Foraging bees returning from the sources do not transfer their nectar directly into the comb, but to a number of receiver bees that, before placing it into the comb, manipulate the nectar with their mouthparts, starting the process of reducing the moisture content of the nectar. More invertase is added to continue the conversion of the sucrose to glucose and fructose. During the transfer the receiver bee extends her tongue and sucks up the nectar that the forager bee has regurgitated. The forager's tongue is not extended. The transferring of nectar to several receiver bees results in efficient use of time, and the faster multiple transfer of information through the colony.

The foraging bee is capable of deciding whether to recruit more foragers or to recruit more receivers, and these interactions have a big impact on the efficiency of exploitation of the nectar resource. If the forager perceives that she is experiencing a long wait for a receiver bee she moves away from the area of the comb where the main nectar transfer activity is being carried out and will often make a tremble dance to recruit more bees to become receivers. If the forager experiences only a short delay she often makes the waggle dance, which serves not only to direct other workers to a specific nectar source, but also to recruit more bees to foraging activities.

The bee colony operates on a decentralised basis with each forager making her own decision as to whether to recruit more foragers or receivers by making waggle and tremble dances. In this way the colony can cope with the nectar flows being brought into it. In summary, the waggle dance recruits more foragers, and the tremble dance recruits more receivers.

Honey bees from different colonies compete with each other for nectar, they are not aggressive to each other, each just tries to gets its share, however aggression is seen when robbing takes place between colonies. Some strains of honey bee are robbers and will actively seek out other colonies to rob them of their stores of honey and nectar if they can gain entrance and not be evicted or killed by the guard bees.

STRATEGIES USED TO WORK FLOWERS FOR NECTAR AND POLLEN

Individual bees do not work at random over a resource, but usually only forage a small area during their foraging life. The size of the area is determined by:
- Plant spacing
- Number of flowers per plant
- Stage of flowering
- Nectar and pollen production
- Weather conditions

- Number of pollinating insects, both for competition for food resource and disturbance to each other

Bees tend to return to the same location for several consecutive trips or days, although the longer the bee forages at a site the greater will be the area it covers. Bees use various cues for identifying worthwhile visits, e.g. the flowers are open, intact, and turgid. Whereas cues for unattractive visits include cessation of nectar or scent production, changes in colour, plant wilting, and petal drop.

Foraging bees employ different strategies to gain access to the pollen and nectar according to the type of flower. In open flowers, e.g. bramble and raspberries, she bites the anthers and uses her forelegs to pull the anthers towards her. In tubular flowers, e.g. ling heather and the disc florets of dandelion, she inserts her proboscis for nectar, and the pollen is incidentally caught on legs and mouthparts. In the case of closed flowers she uses her forelegs to force petals apart, and gathers pollen on her mouthparts and forelegs. In field beans, garden broad beans, and scarlet runner beans, the flower size and the degree of openness of the flower determine whether honey bees can work it by entering at the front of the flower. Bumblebees bite holes in the base of the flower and access the nectar, and honey bees will exploit this using the ready-made holes. This technique is used with aquilegia where nectar collects in the base of the spurs of the flowers. For spike and catkin flowers, e.g. hazel, the worker bee runs along the catkin brushing the pollen onto her body hairs; whilst in presentation flowers, e.g. salvias, the abdomen is pressed against the flower forcing the pollen mass outside the flower and onto the bee's body.

FLOWER FIDELITY OR CONSTANCY

Aristotle observed and recorded flower constancy (fidelity) in honey bees more than 2000 years ago. Honey bees normally fly from one flower to another of the same species, and this has important consequences for the plant and the bee. In the case of the plant, pollen from one species must fertilise the ovule of the same species. For the bee it is also important because when she finds a good source of food she learns the distinctive flower markings, and uses the information to find another flower of the same species. However, between 1–10% of pollen samples have been found with mixed species pollen loads, usually two different species, some of these bees may be scout bees exploring and sampling alternative food sources.

FLOWER CONSTANCY AND LEARNING
BEHAVIOUR IN BEES

Foragers, when not acting as scouts, may not only remain faithful to a single flower type, but often to an area as small as 2.8-3.8 m^2 for their entire foraging life (2-3 weeks in the summer). Once bees are conditioned to a type of flower visit they tend to remain constant to it collecting either pollen or nectar or both. Observations on the foraging population of an entire hive show that the foraging force often divides into groups, each group having its own scouts. Through sociality and communication the scouting force can alert the colony to changes as they occur, and the bees are ready to exploit a new or better source of food as a result. The workers of the whole colony may therefore forage on a variety of plant species.

During her foraging life a bee will tend to keep to one type of foraging behaviour (nectar or pollen collection). However, flowers that offer pollen rewards at one time of the day and nectar rewards at another can trigger a behavioural change in an individual bee, causing her to collect both during the course of a day, e.g. apple and sunflower. Whereas others, e.g. field bean, and red clover, can trigger bees to collect either pollen or nectar only and desert the crop rather than change their foraging behaviour. Different colonies have differing innate preferences for different flower species, and the odour of the food stored in the combs at a particular time can influence the bee's choice of forage source.

In summary, adaptability enables individual bees and the colony as a whole to exploit the most favourable nectar and pollen sources available at any one time.

PLANTS POISONOUS TO BEES
AND DISTASTEFUL HONEYS

In general poisoning by plant substances is not a problem for honey bees foraging in the British Isles, although toxic substances occur in the nectar of rhododendrons, azaleas, and their relatives. Poisoning and death can be caused by red chestnut, some species of lime, particularly the non-native pendant silver lime, and *Tilia orbicularis*; in all these species bumblebees appear to be more affected than honey bees. Native limes including the small-leaved lime and large-leaved lime are not poisonous and may safely be planted for bees.

Honey produced from ragwort nectar is a rich golden colour, but its taste is unpleasant to the human palate, although it improves on keeping. Honey from privet nectar has a strong, bitter flavour and will spoil any other honey with which it is mixed.

Pollination and Fertilisation

DEFINITIONS

Pollination is the prelude to fertilisation and involves the transfer of pollen by an agent, e.g. the honey bee, from the anther to the receptive stigma, usually of another flower of the same species.

Fertilisation is the fusion of the male and female gametes. The pollen grain germinates to produce a pollen tube that grows through the tissues of the stigma and the style, transporting the two male nuclei to the ovule (egg). The pollen tube passes through the micropyle to enter the ovule where it penetrates the nucellus, and ruptures at the tip of the embryo sac liberating the two nuclei, one of which fuses with the nucleus of the ovule, the second with the endosperm nucleus. (fig. 37, page 80).

THE RELATIVE MERITS OF CROSS AND SELF-POLLINATION

Cross-pollination, i.e. the transfer of pollen from one individual to the stigma of another individual of the same species leads to cross-fertilisation, and has the advantage of increasing the amount of genetic variation through new combinations of genes, which may be passed onto the next generation. This is called outbreeding. By increasing the amount of genetic variation and passing beneficial genes to its progeny, a species increases its chances of survival in changing environmental conditions. Natural selection then eliminates those individuals that are less well adapted to change. The price of the advantage of increasing genetic variation is that outbreeding plants need to produce enough pollen to ensure successful pollination, as much will be wasted during transfer by the vector.

Self-pollination, leading to self-fertilisation, has the potential for greater reliability, particularly where members of the species are uncommon and are separated by large distances. It is not dependent on insects, other agents, or the wind to deliver the pollen and can be very useful in places of harsh climate where there are few insects. However, self-fertilisation leads to an extreme form of inbreeding, and can result in less vigorous offspring that may be less able to adapt.

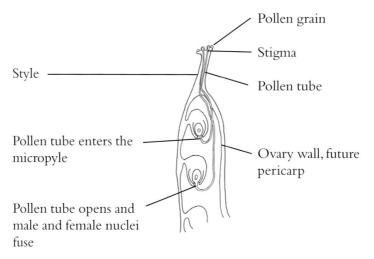

Style

Pollen tube enters the micropyle

Pollen tube opens and male and female nuclei fuse

Pollen grain

Stigma

Pollen tube

Ovary wall, future pericarp

Figure 37. Diagram of stages in fertilisation.

ENSURING CROSS-POLLINATION THROUGH BEES

Bees and bee-pollinated flowering plants depend on each other whilst operating to benefit their own interests. There is a cost benefit equation that must balance for each party.

Nectar and pollen production are costly in energy terms for a plant, and must be balanced by their value in maximising the chance of reproduction. For example, individual flowers must offer enough reward to attract pollinators, but provide as small a quantity as possible so that the pollinators must visit many plants and thereby achieve cross-pollination. Some plants do this by making heavy nectar rewards available only in a small percentage of the flowers of an individual plant.

From the bees' point of view flight and foraging activity are energetically costly and must be balanced by the calories and other nutrients derived from nectar and pollen. Bees make very efficient pollinators because their diet of nectar and pollen is entirely derived from flowers, and hence they focus their food gathering activities on plants yielding these foods. Plants that are wind-pollinated do not need agents such as bees, and this is reflected in their characteristics. The following table compares some of the characteristics of each.

Table 9 TYPICAL CHARACTERISTICS OF WIND AND INSECT POLLINATED FLOWERS

TYPICAL WIND POLLINATED FLOWER	TYPICAL INSECT POLLINATED FLOWER
Small petals not brightly coloured (usually green), or absent; flowers inconspicuous	Large coloured petals; flowers usually conspicuous. If inconspicuous they may be gathered together into inflorescences
Not scented	Scented
Nectaries absent	Nectaries present
Large branched and feathery stigma hanging outside the flower to trap pollen	Small stigma, sticky to hold pollen and enclosed within the flower
Stamens hanging outside the flower to release pollen	Stamens enclosed within the flower
Anthers attached only at midpoint to the tip of the filament so that they swing freely in air currents	Anthers usually fixed at their bases or fused to the filaments along their backs so that they are immovable
Large quantities of pollen produced because of high wastage	Smaller quantities of pollen produced
Pollen grains relatively light, small and dry, often with smooth walls	Pollen grains relatively heavy and large. Sculptured and sticky outside layers help attachment to the insect body
Flower structure relatively simple	Complex structural modifications for particular insects often occur
Flowers frequently borne well above the foliage on long stalks (e.g. many British trees)	Position and time of appearance of the flowers is variable in relation to foliage, though borne above it for increased conspicuousness

PLANT MECHANISMS FAVOURING CROSS-POLLINATION

Dioecious plants have male and female flowers on separate plants and self-pollination is therefore unlikely, e.g. holly and skimmia. Monoecious plants have separate male and female flowers on the same plant and this favours cross-pollination but selfing may also occur, e.g. alder and hazel. In most hermaphrodite flowers (male and female parts present in each flower) there are structural features that favour cross- pollination. In insect pollinated flowers the stigmas are usually borne above the anthers thus reducing the chances of pollen from the same flower falling onto its stigma. As the insect moves into the flower in search of nectar, pollen is either brushed against it or falls onto it before it leaves the flower. An insect visiting the flower may be carrying pollen from another flower of the same species, and will touch the stigma before the anthers as it enters the flower, e.g. white dead-nettle. Special floral structural arrangements, such as heterostyly as in purple-loosestrife, together with such mechanisms as protandry or protogyny, ensure cross-pollination is achieved.

PROTANDRY AND PROTOGYNY

In order to prevent self-pollination, in some plants the anthers and the stigmas mature at different times. If the anthers mature first this is called protandry, whereas protogyny is where the stigmas mature first. Flowers are most commonly protandrous, and examples include white dead-nettle, sages, and members of the Apiaceae, and the Asteraceae. Protogyny occurs in figwort and bluebell. In most cases there is an overlapping period when both anthers and stigmas are ripe, thus allowing selfing to occur if cross-pollination has been unsuccessful. Unusually in hawthorn fertilisation of the ovule takes place before the maturity and dehiscence of the anthers in the same flower.

SELF-INCOMPATIBILITY (SELF-STERILITY)

Self-incompatibility can follow where self-pollination occurs, because the pollen grains do not develop or grow only very slowly, so reducing the chances of self-fertilisation. Self-incompatibility genes inhibit the growth of the pollen tube and ensure outbreeding.

POLLINATION OF FRUIT, VEGETABLES, AND CROPS

Of the 170 agricultural and horticultural crops on which pollination research has been published, 84% are dependent on, or benefit from insect pollination for fruit or seed production. Bees are particularly important pollinators, and bumblebees are especially efficient as they fly at much lower temperatures than honey bees which will tend not to fly for pollen and nectar collection if the temperature is below 12°C.

Honey bees are the main managed pollinator for field crops, and are increasingly relied upon as the distribution and abundance of wild bees diminishes. But managed honey bees too are becoming less numerous because of decreasing numbers of beekeepers, a trend intensified by the impact of the mite *Varroa destructor* on honey bee colonies. Encouragingly this trend may be halted in the future through the increasing interest in bees and beekeeping reported by beekeeping associations.

GENERAL PRINCIPLES FOR CROP POLLINATION

In crop pollination it is good practice to use inexperienced bees that are unfamiliar with the areas around the crop. This is to ensure they will work the crop, and not be distracted by more interesting forage that may be available locally. Before taking colonies to the crop to be pollinated it is advisable to keep the bees at least 3 km (approx. 2 miles) away rather than at the crop site throughout the year. The hives should not be moved onto the crop until it has begun flowering. They should be placed on stands, never positioned in low lying areas prone to damp air pockets, and they should be protected from strong winds by bales of straw, hedges, or other forms of windbreak. They should be orientated to face the early sun as this stimulates early foraging, important for the pollination of many crops as they may have flowers whose stigmas are receptive early in the morning. Bees prefer to work within 100 m of their colony, although they will fly several kilometres if necessary. By placing the colonies throughout the crop if convenient, it is possible to ensure that the whole crop area is accessible.

POLLINATION OF FRUIT CROPS BY BEES

Some species and varieties of fruit can produce adequate crops when self-pollinated, examples include blackcurrant, peach, nectarine, apricot, and sour cherry. However, many fruit varieties are only partially self-fertile and produce more and better quality fruits when fertilised through cross-pollination, examples include strawberry, plum, and blueberry. Species such as apples and pears require donor pollen from named varieties, and knowledge of this is important when planting an orchard or even a few fruit trees in a produce garden. Adequate pollination is required to reduce the risk of misshapen fruit, e.g. strawberry and blackberry and apple. Fruits such as strawberry require many pollen grains to ensure the fertilisation of the many ovules which will develop into small pips or achenes on the outside of the swollen receptacle that forms the flesh of the strawberry (fig. 40, page 84). Where there is only one seed in the fruit, e.g. stone fruits like cherry and plum, in theory only a single compatible pollen grain is required.

Figure 38. LS Strawberry *(Fragaria spp.)* flower

Carpel

Stamen

Receptacle

Petal

Stigma

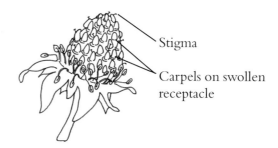

Figure 39. Strawberry flower at the time of petal fall

Stigma

Carpels on swollen receptacle

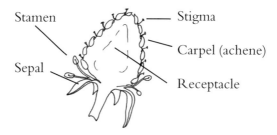

Figure 40. LS Strawberry fruit (a berry)

Stamen

Sepal

Stigma

Carpel (achene)

Receptacle

BEE BEHAVIOUR ON FRUIT FLOWERS AND
ITS IMPACT ON POLLINATION EFFECTIVENESS

Many of the visits bees make to the flowers of fruit trees do not lead to pollination, either because the bees do not touch the stigmas, or because the parts of the bee bodies that do touch them are not carrying compatible pollen. Much depends on whether the bee visiting the flower is collecting nectar or pollen. Nectar gatherers tend to keep their bodies more free of pollen than pollen gatherers and so are less likely to pollinate.

Whether or not nectar gatherers pollinate flowers of the trees they visit depends on where they stand and move about on the flowers. Bees collecting nectar stand either on the anthers, petals, or both and push their heads down towards the nectaries. Nectar gatherers standing on the anthers often touch the stigmas and so may pollinate the flowers with pollen they are carrying, whilst receiving pollen from the flower being visited. However, when the nectar gatherer stands on the petals of some flowers, she may fail to touch the stigmas when approaching the nectaries. Although when visiting flowers with spreading stamens, e.g. plum, pear, peach, and apricot, she may get pollen onto her body, a nectar gatherer standing on the petals of apple flowers that have stiff upright stamens probably will not touch the anthers, nor get dusted with pollen. Some apple flowers can only be approached from the side because the thickness of the anther filaments differs from one variety to another, and a barrier of thick filaments may make it difficult for bees to reach nectaries when trying to access them from the top. Generally, pollen gatherers are more valuable as pollinators than nectar gatherers, they also work faster spending less time at each flower.

POLLINATION OF FRUIT TREES

In the British Isles fruit flowering time often coincides with cold, wet, windy weather in which honey bees are reluctant to fly. It is therefore essential for the beekeeper to ensure that when the weather is favourable there are enough bees available to effect the pollination.

The number of colonies required for pollinating fruit trees is dependent on the weather, the age of the orchard, the fruit species, varieties of fruit, the relative attractiveness of other flowers in the neighbourhood, and the number of other pollinators in surrounding areas. A rule of thumb is to provide 2-3 colonies per ha of fruit to be pollinated. Colonies for fruit pollination should contain no less than 5 frames with developing brood at all stages. Colonies having young brood to feed should be selected as they will be preferentially collecting pollen. This may make it necessary to feed sugar syrup to satisfy the nectar requirement of the colony. It is possible through breeding to select honey bees that have a high pollen hoarding behaviour, and hence visit many flowers to gather their pollen. Bees tend to forage near their hives, and the number of bees diminishes quite rapidly with increasing distance. Honey bees prefer to work up and down rather than across rows, especially where adjacent rows are of different varieties, and hence there is a need to locate the hives appropriately. Ideally the hives should be spaced singly throughout the orchard, but this is time consuming to manage and therefore a compromise practice is to distribute evenly spaced groups of 4 -5 colonies.

Taking the colonies to the orchard or plantation should be delayed until flowering begins, this prevents bees from becoming habituated to flowers other than the target crop. For example, bees will work dandelions preferentially if present beneath the fruit trees.

In the case of apples, at least 6-7 of the ovules in the flower must be fertilised or else the fruit may be misshapen, small, or may fall before ripe. Flowering crab apples can be used as a universal pollen donor, and because of this they are very useful in rejuvenating the productivity of old orchards. Younger trees have fewer blossoms and are less attractive to bees than older trees, so the grower with an orchard of young apple trees needs to increase the number of hives to compensate, usually by doubling them.

Pears produce abundant pollen but little nectar and so most honey bees visiting pears are pollen collectors. Most pear varieties are self-sterile and need cross-pollination with another variety, usually one that is specifically used as a pollen donor. If other forage is available honey bees may neglect pears, and this reduction in bee visits has to be overcome also by doubling the number of colonies that would be used for mature apples.

In plums the stigma is receptive as soon as the flower opens, but the anthers only release pollen when the flowers become fully open, staying open for 3-5 days. Most plum varieties require cross-pollination with a suitable pollen donor, although there are completely self-fertile varieties. Honey bees usually work plum flowers in the morning.

SOFT FRUIT POLLINATION

Raspberries are moderately self-fertile and crossing and selfing are possible in the same flower. Because the raspberry is an aggregate fruit it requires multiple bee visits to adequately pollinate all the ovules in the flower. Strawberry flowers produce nectar and pollen, but they are not always attractive to honey bees so a higher density of colonies is required in strawberry fields, as a guide this should be 9 per ha.

FIELD POLLINATION OF VEGETABLE AND OTHER CROPS

Where crops are grown for edible fruits, vegetables, or seeds, insect pollination usually benefits yield, e.g. aubergines, peppers, tomatoes, and some beans.

Bees should be brought in when there are enough flowers to attract them. However, in the case of the French bean self-pollination is the norm, and this happens at or before flower opening in the morning; but, during the time taken for the pollen tube to grow, bees can visit the flower so cross-pollination and out-breeding is possible.

Most varieties of oil-seed rape grown in the British Isles are self-fertile and seed set is good whether the plant is self or cross-pollinated. However, cross-pollination using honey bees is known to increase the set of early flowers, the evenness of ripening, and thus ease of harvesting. Usual colony density should be 5/ha. Oil-seed rape is sown in both winter and spring, and nectar and pollen flows may be experienced from April until at least August in some years and locations.

Mustard is grown commercially for culinary seed in small quantities in eastern England, and is also grown elsewhere as a green manure and for game cover. Borage is grown extensively in East Yorkshire and some other parts of the British Isles, and will flower and secrete from July / August until the fields are swathed or the re-growth after cutting is stopped by frost. The seeds are crushed, and the oil extracted is used in the pharmaceutical industry.

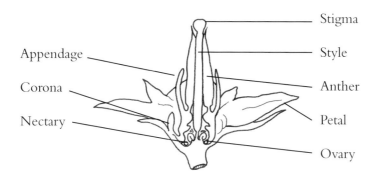

Figure 41. LS Borage *(Borago officinalis)* flower

SEED PROPAGATION AND BREEDING

Some crops being grown for seed propagation require cross-pollination to produce viable seed, e.g. cabbages, kale, Brussels sprouts, kohl-rabi, cauliflower, sprouting broccoli, beet, carrot, celery, parsnip, lettuce, onion, and leek. Pollination and yield are optimised where flowers receive multiple bee visits over several days.

Plant breeding trials and commercial seed production are usually set out with rows of plants that will be the pollen donors (male), alternated with rows (two or three depending on the species) of the female plants from which the seed will be harvested. Bees tend to work down rows, and in seed production it is important to get them to work across the rows to visit both male and female plants; hives should be placed to encourage this by dispersing them throughout the crop. Colony density should be 5 per ha. Precautions may be necessary where the maintenance of varietal purity is important.

POLLINATION OF CROPS AND SEED PRODUCTION IN GLASSHOUSES USING HONEY BEES

A number of crops that are grown under glasshouse conditions benefit from pollination by honey bees. These include strawberries where 1-2 colonies per 1000m^2 are recommended. High value flower and vegetable seeds are also produced under controlled glasshouse conditions. Possibly as a result of global warming, problems with the quality and yield of seed produced in Italy and France has resulted in seed companies investigating more locations for commercial seed production in the British Isles. Potential seed crops include white cabbage, radicchio, chicory, cauliflowers, leeks, onions, and kohl-rabi. Pollination of such crops requires around 2 colonies per glasshouse area of 300m^2. For seed propagation and breeding the setting out of plants under glass is similar to that used for field grown crops.

Placing colonies inside the glasshouse can lead to significant losses of foraging bees flying up to the roof of the glasshouse, becoming disorientated, and lost to the colony. However if colonies are provided with two entrances, one entrance with direct access into the glasshouse, and one entrance directly to the outside, losses of bees are reduced significantly. Older bees that were foraging before they were brought to the glasshouse will use the entrance to the outside, relocating, after flying, to that entrance and will not become trapped inside the glasshouse. Some younger foraging bees are attracted to the entrance facing the crop to be pollinated. They learn to forage inside the glasshouse thus pollinating the crop, relocate to that entrance, and never go outside the glasshouse. As well as providing the pollination service, for which a fee is sometimes paid, a honey crop can also be taken from some of these glasshouse crops. Nectar from onion or leek flowers produces a honey that initially tastes of onion, but this flavour is lost after storage.

More detailed information on crop pollination can be found in 'Crop Pollination by Bees'. Delaplane and Mayer (2000).

Bee Forage and Conservation

INTRODUCTION

This chapter considers some of the options for promoting bee conservation and bee forage, and although the book is primarily concerned with honey bees, the habitat improvements and the choices of plant species recommended will also help many other beneficial insects, including bumblebees and hoverflies. Before considering the options for retaining and improving plant biodiversity, the chapter identifies some of the changes that have taken place in the agricultural landscape and built environment.

CHANGES IN THE LANDSCAPE DUE TO AGRICULTURE

The landscape of the British Isles has been shaped by agriculture, and has changed in response to farming practices over many centuries. The development of modern capital-intensive farming in the 20th Century, particularly since the 1950s, has greatly accelerated the processes effecting widespread and profound changes to the landscape. This intensification was aided by post World War 2 UK agricultural policy, the aim of which was to achieve high levels of self-sufficiency in temperate crops. The legislation for this was initiated by the 1947 Agriculture Act, and followed in 1976 by the government publication 'Food from our own Resources'.

Substantial degradation in biodiversity has resulted from this intensification, leading to a significant impact on the availability of bee forage. New farming methods, increased monoculture, and the use of pesticides, herbicides, and inorganic fertilisers have been used to enhance crop yields. The result has been the amalgamation of fields, the removal of hedges, and conversion of permanent pasture to arable land, the loss of species-rich grassland through 'improvement', the loss of arable weed species, woodland clearance, drainage of wetlands, and ploughing up of lowland heath and heather moorland. Legislation to protect the most sensitive and valuable of these habitats has failed to protect many of them given the impetus of agricultural intensification.

By the 1980s the extent and impact of these changes led to UK government and European Common Agricultural Policy changes based upon an emerging recognition that farming practice must become more sensitive to its environmental impacts. Legislation, in particular the 1981 Wildlife and Countryside Act, together with government-funded schemes, targeted the protection of the most valuable habitats. These aimed to combine stronger statutory protection with financial incentives offered to land managers and farmers who were prepared to agree to environmentally beneficial management practices. The first national scheme was the Environmentally Sensitive Area (ESA) programme to target areas where traditional farming practices needed to continue if valuable habitats were to be sustained.

By the early 1990s continued environmental deterioration led to further government and Common Agricultural Policy change. A new generation of funding programmes, particularly Countryside Stewardship, introduced by the Countryside Commission in 1991, and adopted as mainstream government policy in 1996, extended the scope of management agreements and funding. Subsequently these schemes have been consolidated and extended to increase participation and pro-active management to encourage biodiversity.

Current programmes have a number of benefits for bee species including:
- Sympathetic management and enhancement of species-rich grasslands that are vital in sustaining viable populations of many insect species, including bees.
- Habitat re-creation, including the conversion of intensively managed grasslands and arable land to create valuable habitats, for example, herb-rich meadowland.
- The management of field margins in arable crops to foster biodiversity.
- The creation of rough grassland to provide nest and hibernation sites.
- The conservation and restoration of heather moorland.

CHANGES IN THE LANDSCAPE DUE TO DEVELOPMENT AND THE BUILT ENVIRONMENT

The building of houses, warehousing, distribution, and out of town shopping centres, and roads to cater for the ever increasing volume of traffic, have all made a significant impact on the landscape and consequently on the forage available to bees. This resulting road infrastructure causes many wildlife road casualties, including bees, that because of their small body size go unnoticed.

Recent years have seen a big growth of interest in gardens and outdoor living spaces, together with the greening of the urban and suburban environments through local authority and government schemes, and the activities of non-governmental organisations. This has resulted in some situations where honey bees kept in urban and suburban locations do much better than those kept in locations where there is intensive agriculture.

THE CHANGING FLORA

The flora of the British Isles is undergoing continual change. This change is being monitored by botanists and the most recent results are described in the 'New Atlas of the British and Irish Flora' published in 2002. The atlas is based on a major survey carried out between the years 1987-1999; it compares the changes in the frequency and distribution of plant species since the previous extensive surveys that were carried out in the 1950s. The 'Changing Flora of the UK' written by Preston et al and published in 2002 by the Department of the Environment, Food and Rural Affairs (Defra), concluded that the major causes of change in the UK flora over the last 40 years are:

*   Increasing levels of nutrient availability across a range of habitats.
*   Habitat loss, particularly through the conversion of species-rich plant communities to less species-rich habitats as a result of agricultural intensification or afforestation.
*   A decrease in mixed farming with an increased tendency to livestock farming in the north and west, and to arable farming in the south and east.
*   The spread of introduced species and garden escapees.

Species introduced into the British Isles by man before AD1500 are called archaeophytes, those introduced in recent times are known as neophytes. Native species and archaeophytes, such as weeds of arable crops and early food and medicinal plants, generally occurring in arable farmland, horticultural land, calcareous grassland, dwarf shrub heath, bogs, and mountain habitats have decreased in frequency. Neophytes, especially trees and shrubs, generally associated with improved grasslands, built-up areas, and gardens have increased in frequency. This effect has not yet occurred to the same degree in the Scottish Highlands as in the rest of the British Isles, and the research has shown other regional differences. Plants with a northerly global distribution have decreased in frequency especially in England, Wales, and Northern Ireland, whereas those with a Mediterranean distribution have prospered. There has been a decline in the number of species typical of locations where nutrient levels are low, and a corresponding increase in species typical of areas where nutrient levels are higher. Tall species have been more successful than short species, and this may be because tall species compete with the smaller species and crowd them out.

THE POTENTIAL IMPACT OF GLOBAL WARMING

Phenology is the study of periodicity phenomena in plants, e.g. flowering times; it is a tool being used to examine the belief that global warming is taking place. In May 2002 Fitter and Fitter published a paper that showed evidence of changes taking place in the flowering times of British plants. Data from observations made of the first flowering date for a set of 557 plant species recorded over a 47 year period at a single location in south central England were analysed. The results show that the average first flowering date of 385 of them has advanced by 4.5 days during the past decade compared with the previous four decades. Other differences were also observed. White dead-nettle, a species important for bumblebees, used to flower occasionally in the winter, but now flowers regularly throughout the winter months.

The study looked at the relationship of first flowering date with climatic variables and found that this date is sensitive to the temperature in the previous month, with spring flowering species being the most responsive. The authors concluded that temperature, or possibly a climatic variable correlated with it, such as sunshine hours, is a key determinant of flowering time. Of particular relevance to bees and beekeeping is that early flowering insect-pollinated species are much more sensitive to warming than those that flower later. The potential impact of these phenological changes could be of significance to beekeeping, with the prospect of pollen and nectar sources being available to bees for a season extended at both ends if the ambient temperature is high enough for them to forage successfully.

The potential impact of global warming on UK gardens has been considered in the report on 'Gardening in the Global Greenhouse, the impacts of climate change on gardens in the UK', published in November 2002 under the UK Climate Impacts Programme (UKCIP). A number of scenarios were described, together with likely changes in garden styles caused by climatic changes. These could have a significant effect on the availability and timing of bee forage.

BRITISH FLORAL SOURCES FOR HONEY BEES

Honey bee colonies are kept throughout the British Isles, and the pattern of beekeeping varies in relation to the forage available. For example, for some beekeepers the main honey-yielding crops may be oil-seed rape and field beans, whilst for others it may be heather or clover.

For honey bee colonies to thrive they need a regular supply of nectar and, more importantly, continuity of pollen availability throughout the active season. Many beekeepers migrate their colonies to forage sources, especially high value honey crops such as ling heather. The disadvantage of this is that moving bees can stress them, and increase their susceptibility to diseases such as Nosema *(Nosema apis)* and its associated bee virus diseases.

The following table lists major and minor honey bee forage plants to be found in the British Isles. These flowering times can only be general observations because of the variation across the British Isles. Beekeepers have to adapt their beekeeping practices to take advantage of these sources, and in general it can be said that bees thrive where there is a continual supply of nectar and pollen throughout the brood-rearing season.

Table 10. BRITTISH FLORAL SOURCES OF IMPORTANCE TO HONEY BEES

PLANT NAME	Feb/Mar	Apr	May	Jun	July	Aug	Sep/Oct
Alder (P)	•						
Almond	•						
Alyssum		•					
Anchusa				•			
Apple★			•				
Arabis		•					
Ash (P)		•					
Aubretia		•					
Autumn crocus							•
Balsam						•	•
Beech (P)			•				
Bell heather★					•	•	
Berberis		•					
Bergamot					•		
Bilberry			•				
Bindweed				•			
Birch (P)			•				
Bird's-foot-trefoil				•			
Blackberry★					•	•	
Blackthorn		•					
Bluebell			•				
Borage★					•	•	•
Brassicas			•	•	•	•	
Broom			•				
Buttercup				•			
Campanula					•	•	
Cat-mint				•			
Ceanothus			•				
Celandine	•						
Cherry★		•					
Crab apple		•					
Crane's-bill				•	•		

PLANT NAME	Feb/Mar	April	May	Jun	Jul	Aug	Sep/Oct
Crocus	•						
Currants		•					
Damson★		•					
Dandelion★			•	•			
Dead-nettle[3]	•		•	•	•		
Doronicum		•					
Dwarf gorse						•	•
Elm	•						
Escallonia					•		
Fennel					•		
Field bean★				•			
Figwort					•		
Forget-me-not			•				
Fuschia						•	•
Golden rod					•		
Gooseberry		•					
Gorse			•				
Hawthorn★			•				
Hazel (P)	•						
Hogweed					•		
Holly			•				
Hollyhock					•		
Horse-chestnut			•				
Ivy★[2]							•
Jacob's-ladder				•			
Knapweed				•			
Laurel		•					
Lavender					•	•	
Lime★				•	•		
Ling heather★						•	•
Lucerne				•			
Mallow					•		

94

PLANT NAME	Feb/Mar	Apr	May	Jun	July	Aug	Sept/Oct
Maple★		•					
Marjoram						•	
Meadowsweet (P)				•	•	•	
Michaelmas daisy						•	•
Mint						•	
Mullein						•	
Mustard						•	
Oak			•				
Oil-seed rape autumn sown★		•	•				
Oil-seed rape spring sown★				•	•		
Onion				•			
Pear★		•					
Phacelia★				•	•		
Plantain			•				
Plum★		•					
Poppy (P)					•		
Privet					•		
Prunus	•						
Purple-loosestrife						•	
Pyracantha				•			
Ragwort					•		
Raspberry★				•			
Red clover★						•	
Robinia				•			
Rock-rose (P)				•			
Sage					•	•	
Scabious					•	•	
Sea-lavender[1]						•	
Snowdrop	•						
Sunflower						•	

95

PLANT NAME	Feb/Mar	Apr	May	Jun	July	Aug	Sep/Oct
Sweet Chestnut					•		
Sycamore★			•				
Thistle						•	
Thrift			•				
Thyme				•			
Toadflax						•	
Traveller's joy						•	
Veronica					•		
Vetch				•			
Violet	•						
Viper's bugloss				•			
Virginia creeper						•	
Wallflower			•				
White bryony				•			
White clover★				•	•		
Wild rose (P)				•			
Willow	•						
Willowherb★					•	•	
Winter aconite	•						
Winter heaths	•						
Wood anemone		•					
Wood sage						•	
Yellow melilot				•			

(P) – Pollen Source only

★ – Major bee plant, widespread or locally significant

1 – In coastal regions sea lavender will yield good nectar producing a light coloured honey

2 – Ivy can produce a useful supply of nectar from October until the first frosts.

3 – White dead-nettle regularly flowers throughout winter months

CONSERVATION OF BEES

When considering how to develop schemes that will benefit bee conservation it is important to know the life cycles of bee species, and understand the habitats and resources they need to complete them. Bees are characterised by the degree of sociality they exhibit. Most species of bees are non-social/solitary, where a single female makes a nest for her offspring, and collects the food (pollen and nectar) needed for their development, without the co-operation of a caste of worker bees. Individuals of truly solitary species never have contact with their offspring, as they die leaving them to over-winter as pupae. In bumblebee species only the queen survives to establish a new colony in the following year.

Social bees, for example honey bees (highly eusocial), live in colonies that over-winter. 'Bees of the World', O'Toole and Raw (1991), contains an excellent description of the different types and behaviours of bees throughout the world.

WHAT DO BEES NEED?

- Undisturbed nesting sites.
- Solitary bees may burrow into the ground, into mortar in brick and stonework, or use hollow bramble stems, or beetle borings in rotten wood.
- Increasingly, artificial purpose-built 'homes' are being provided by conservation minded people.
- Social bees, such as bumblebees, may construct their nests in old mouse, vole and mole holes; under hedge vegetation; beneath moss or grass tussocks, and under piles of cut vegetation.
- Honey bees will use beehives, cavities in old trees or walls, roof spaces and chimneys.
- Locations where the queen bumblebees can over-winter, dry and undisturbed.
- Consistent supplies of pollen and nectar sources from early spring to late autumn.
- Unpolluted water.

GENERAL LAND MANAGEMENT PRINCIPLES THAT WILL HELP BEE CONSERVATION

- Do not cultivate right up to the field edge; leave margins of established vegetation as undisturbed areas for bees.
- Use selective herbicides to kill specific invasive species, and apply them locally to the 'weedy' patches, i.e. leave as many flowers and grasses as possible.

- Avoid spray drift from herbicides and insecticides.
- On areas where bees already exist, or might colonise, use caution when mowing, and avoid a summer cut; delay it at least until August, preferably September if possible, to protect surface nesting bees.
- Encourage wild flowers and consider sowing wildflower seed mixtures using native species, preferably of local origin, on land where the existing flora is poor.

MEASURES THAT ARE OF PARTICULAR VALUE FOR BEES

The following measures can help in both encouraging bees in areas where meadows or pastures are rare or absent, and in providing continuity of habitat throughout the year. They can be used in farmland, private and publicly owned land, large gardens and roadside verges.

- Allow natural regeneration where there is a sufficient seed bank.
- Sow annual game cover strips, e.g. phacelia, teasel, linseed, mustard, and borage can be used. Phacelia is best planted on its own because it can out-compete other species planted with it.
- Encourage forage plants in hedgerows, ditch banks, and woodlands.
- Sow wildflower and grass mixtures in field margins or blocks of approximately 1ha. These should include red clover, bird's-foot-trefoil, and sainfoin. Field margins can be sown in 2 or 6 metre strips.

2 metre grass margins:
Thick tussock grass margins provide:
- Food during the spring/summer period.
- Sites for both surface nesting bees, and those that burrow into grass tussocks.
- Hibernation sites.

Mowing is best carried out between October and February where practical. This protects food in spring and summer, avoids damage to nests, and minimises the destruction of queens that hibernate at ground level. Good hedgerow management in association with grass margins further improves bee conservation.

6 metre permanent grass margins
Follow the guidelines above for the 2 metre margins on 2m of the strip, and leave this undisturbed and uncut from the end of February to October to protect surface nesting bees, and those that burrow under the grass. Cut the remaining 4 metres in late July / August.

Annex III lists recommended wildflower and grass seed mixtures that can be used in these schemes according to soil type.

WILD FLOWERS THAT ATTRACT BEES

For short-tongued bumblebees the Rosaceae, Onagraceae, and Asteraceae are the most important families, whilst longer-tongued bees can also utilise members of the Lamiaceae, Fabaceae, and Scrophulariaceae. Special mention must be made of the importance of white dead-nettle as a bumblebee forage plant for queens emerging from hibernation in spring.

Foxglove, woundwort, and honeysuckle are suitable bee plants for shady field edges. Marsh thistle, water figwort, and marsh woundwort are suitable for wet areas and ditch banks. Black horehound can be sown along hedgerows, field and roadside edges.

Before introducing wild flowers, or changing land management regimes to encourage them, it is important to confirm that this will not damage or disrupt existing valuable wildlife habitats or contravene legislation. If there is any uncertainty take specialist advice from the relevant government conservation advisors or county wildlife trusts. Seeds should be from native species and ideally of local origin.

TREES FOR BEES

The nectar and pollen sources from trees make an important contribution to the forage available to all bee species. Where trees are present in hedgerows, hedge management should ensure that the trees are not cut back when the hedge is trimmed, and hedgerow plants are allowed to flower and fruit. This will benefit not only bees and other insects but birds as well.

Orchards are also important for the forage available from the fruit blossom and the perennial herbaceous species. Some tree species that can be used in appropriate agricultural areas and town or garden planting, together with their approximate flowering period, are listed in Annex IV. It should be noted that many trees grow too large for gardens, and care should be taken to find out about their growth rate and eventual height when making a selection.

PLANTS FOR GARDENS

Gardens no matter how large or small can be planted with species that will not only benefit bees, but also attract bird, and other animal species to feed on the berries, fruits, and seeds produced from some of these plants. Examples are listed in Annex V.

Hooper and Taylor 'The Beekeepers' Garden' (1988) provides comprehensive information on suitable plants, also useful is the classic text of Howes, 'Plants and Beekeeping', (reprinted in 1979).

Glossary

Actinomorphic – flowers that can be bisected vertically in planes into similar halves. The flowers are said to be radially symmetrical.

Androecium – collective term that refers to the stamens, the male parts of a flower.

Anemophilous – wind pollinated plants where wind is the vector used to move the pollen from plant to plant.

Angiosperms – a group of flowering plants the seeds of which are borne within a mature ovary (fruit). This term has now been replaced by the term Anthophyta. The Anthophyta contains two classes the Monocotyledonae and the Dicotyledonae.

Annuals – plants that complete their life cycle in one year.

Antennal notch – structure found on the basitarsus of the foreleg of the honey bee; it is lined with hairs through which bees draw their antennae to remove pollen.

Anther – the terminal part of a stamen, contains pollen in pollen sacs that is shed when ripe, normally by bursting longitudinally. The pollen grains are the microspores.

Axil – the point at which the base of the upper side of a leaf joins the stem, or where a branch diverges.

Basifixed – fixed at the base, term used to describe how anther lobes are attached to the anther filament.

Basitarsus – the largest subsegment of the tarsus, the tarsus being the last segment in an insect leg.

Bee bread – pollen that has been mixed with nectar and honey, then stored in the comb, usually at the edge of the brood nest.

Bee dances – a highly sophisticated system of communication signals, that are used to regulate nectar and pollen gathering and processing activities.

Biennials – plants that complete their life cycle over a two year period.

Bracts – modified often scale-like leaves with relatively undeveloped blades, in the axil of which arises a flower or a branch or an inflorescence.

Calyx – the outermost envelope of a flower consisting usually of green, leaf-like members (sepals). In the bud stage they enclose and protect the flower.

Capitulum- a thick or dense head or cluster of flowers e.g. dandelion or clover.

Carpel – the female reproductive organ consisting of an ovary that contains one or more ovules (which become seed after fertilisation), and a stigma, the receptive surface for pollen.

Catkin – a form of wind pollinated unisexual inflorescence in which male flowers are often pendulous and female are erect and cone-shaped.

Chasmogamous – flowers that open normally (the opposite of cleistogamous).

Cibarium – hollow cavity in the head of the bee, lined with muscles into which the glossa pumps liquids such as nectar and water.

Cleistogamous – flowers that do not open and are self-pollinated in the bud stage e.g. violet.

Colpus (pl colpi) – an elongated aperture or furrow, usually tapering towards its ends found on the surface of the pollen grains of some plant species.

Connective – the tissue found between the lobes of an anther that holds them together.

Corbicula – also referred to as the pollen basket, an expanded, slightly concave area on the outer surface of each tibia of the worker bee, fringed by hairs on its edges, it has one central bristle upon which the pollen or propolis loads can be anchored.

Corolla – the inner ring or whorl of the perianth within the calyx, consisting of a group of petals.

Cross-pollination – the transfer of pollen from stamens to the stigma of a flower of a different plant of the same species.

Dehiscence – splitting of the anther sacs to liberate their pollen grains.

Dichogamous – condition where the male and female parts of a flower mature at different times, thereby ensuring that self-pollination does not occur.

Dicotyledon – (Dicotyledonae) the larger of the two classes of flowering plants, distinguished by the embryo having two seed leaves (cotyledons). Floral parts are usually in fours or fives.

Dioecious – term applied to unisexual plants in which the male and female flowers are on separate individuals.

Diploid – having two matching sets of chromosomes.

Diurnal – intrinsic internal rhythmic changes occurring with a periodicity of approximately 24 hours, e.g. a flower which opens by day and closes by night.

DNA (deoxyribonucleic acid) – the nucleic acid forming the genetic material of all cells, and a major component of chromosomes.

Dorsifixed – fixed at the back, term used to describe how anther lobes are attached to the anther filament.

Endosperm – the nutritive tissue for the embryo in the developing seed.

Entomophilous – pollination by insects.

Enzyme – a protein chemical produced by a cell that is a catalyst promoting and accelerating one or more specific biochemical reactions in an organism's metabolism.

Epigynous – a flower with an inferior ovary, i.e. the receptacle completely encloses the carpels and the other flower parts arise from the receptacle above it.

Eusocial – term used to describe where insects, such as bees, exhibit cooperative brood care, overlap between generations and have reproductive castes.

Eutrophication – an increase in the nutrient status of a body of water, usually occurring as a result of human activity.

Exine – the outer surface layer of a pollen grain.

Extra-floral nectar – term applied to nectar that is produced by a part of a plant other than the flower.

Family – unit of classification with all its members closely related and sharing major attributes.

Fat bodies – cream-coloured cells found in the dorsal and ventral parts of the abdomen of the honey bee that concentrate and store fat, protein in the form of albumen, and glycogen, that can be rapidly converted to glucose when needed.

Fermentation – breakdown of organic substances (typically sugars and fats) by microorganisms to yield simpler organic chemicals e.g. the production of alcohol from sugar by yeasts.

Fertilisation – fusion of two gametes (male and female). In plants a pollen tube is involved in the fertilisation process.

Filament – the stalk part of an anther.

Flabellum – also called labellum, a small spoon-shaped structure at the end of the bee proboscis that makes contact with nectar, water and honey when feeding.

Flora – a list of plant species (with descriptions) for a particular geographical area, arranged in families and genera, including an identification key.

Follicle – a dry, usually many-seeded fruit, dehiscent along one side and formed from one carpel.

Gametes – haploid cells specialised for fertilisation.

Gamopetalous – (monopetalous) having all the petals joined into one piece.

Gamosepalous – (monosepalous) having all the sepals joined into one piece.

Gymnosperms – a term no longer used in the formal schemes of classification, but still often referred to. The term refers to 'naked seeded plants' where the ovule and the seeds lie exposed.

Gynoecium – also called the pistil, the collective term for the carpels or the female parts of a flower.

Haploid – a single set of chromosomes.

Hemiptera (Rhyncota) – a large order of insects including aphids, and scale insects with mouthparts modified for piercing and sucking.

Hermaphrodite – bisexual, having stamens (male) and pistil (female) within the same flower.

Homogamous – when male and female parts of a flower mature simultaneously.

Hybrids – results of crosses between two species.

Hymenoptera – a large order of insects that includes bees, ants and wasps.

Hypogynous – of a flower having a superior ovary; the calyx, corolla and stamens being inserted at the base of the ovary.

Hypopharyngeal glands – glands located in the head of the worker honey bee. In the young worker bee they produce brood food that is fed to developing larvae, whilst in the older bee they secrete enzymes that convert nectar and honeydew into honey

Inferior – the situation where the ovary is borne below the point of origin of the sepals, petals and stamens and is fused with the surrounding receptacle.

Inflorescence – a group of flowers with their branching system and associated bracts.

Intine – the inner, less deterioration-resistant layer in the wall of a pollen grain.

Intra-specific – within a species.

Inter-specific – between species.

Irregular flower – a flower with irregular symmetry in its parts. Such flowers are always specialised for insect visits.

Keel – The lower two petals of a flower typical of the legume families, that adhere at their margins and somewhat resemble the keel of a boat.

Labiate – a flower having two lips separated by a wide regular opening.

Labium – part of the bee proboscis forming the lower lip.

Legume – one-celled fruit having two valves opening along the face or back, may contain one or many seeds e.g. peas

Mandibles – one of the first pair of mouthparts, principally used in bees for biting and manipulation.

Mandibular glands – a pair of exocrine glands found on each side of the bee's head, each attached to its mandible by a duct. Queen mandibular glands produce queen substance, 9-keto-(E)–2 decenoic acid, the functions of which include inhibition of queen rearing and swarming. Young worker bee mandibular glands produce larval food, particularly 10-hydroxy-2-decenoic acid, the main lipid component of larval food. The glands of older workers change to produce 2-heptanone, an alarm pheromone.

Maxillae – components of the bee's mouthparts

Meiosis – process by which a nucleus divides by two divisions into four nuclei, each containing half the original number of chromosomes.

Melissopalynology – the study of pollen in honey samples.

Micron (micrometre) – one thousandth of a millimetre. Bacteria are about 1μm in diameter.

Micropyle - the minute pore in a seed coat through which water enters at the start of germination.

Microsporangia – in seed plants, the place where the microspores (i.e. pollen grains) develop.

Microspores – pollen grains in seed plants.

Mitosis – process where the division of the cell nucleus produces two genetically identical daughter cells.

Monocotyledon – (Monocotyledonae) distinguished from the Dicotyledonae by having a single seed leaf (cotyledon) in the embryo. The floral parts are usually in threes. Examples include grasses, lilies and tulips.

Monoecious – plants which bear separate male and female flowers on the same individual.

Morphology – the study of the form or appearance of an organism (both internally and externally). Anatomy is one aspect of morphology.

Nectar – a secretion produced from fluid-secreting glands of flowers and attractive to insects and other pollinating vectors such as moths.

Nectaries – glands or secreting tissue in plants that produce nectar.

Nosema – a disease of adult honey bees the causal agent of which is a Microsporan called *Nosema apis*.

Nototribic – flowers which are adapted to deposit their pollen on the back of the pollinating insect whilst visiting the flower.

Nucellus – tissue that surrounds the ovule, and provides food for the seed.

Nucleus – the structure in a cell that contains the cell's chromosomes (genetic material).

Outbreeding – mechanisms that promote genetic variability thereby enabling evolutionary selection to select the fittest combinations of genes. Mechanisms favouring outbreeding include dichogamy, heterostyly and incompatibility.

Ovary – the basal part of the gynoecium containing the ovules.

Ovule – the organ that contains the embryo-sac which contains the egg and develops into the seed after fertilisation. The megaspore produces the embryo-sac.

Pappus – ring of fine hairs developing from the calyx and fruits of the Asteraceae e.g. dandelion.

Pedicel – the stalk of a flower.

Perennials – plants that grow and flower in successive years.

Perianth – the outer parts of a flower enclosing the stamens and anthers. In the Dicotyledonae this is differentiated into the calyx (usually green) and the corolla (often brightly coloured). In the Monocotyledonae usually there is no differentiation.

Pericarp – wall of an ovary after it has matured into a fruit which may be hard e.g. a nut, or fleshy e.g. a berry.

Perigynous – of a flower with a superior ovary with the calyx, corolla and stamens inserted above the base of an ovary on an extension of the receptacle that is not fused with the ovary.

Petal – one of the parts forming the corolla of the flower, often brightly coloured.

Petaloid – petal-like.

Phenology – the study of periodicity in plants, such as the timing of flowering in relation to the climate.

Phloem – the main food-conducting tissue in vascular plants.

Phylogenetics – an approach to biological classification concerned with reconstructing the evolutionary history of a group of organisms.

Phylogeny – evolutionary history.

Pinna – a leaflet of a pinnate leaf.

Pistil – the female organ in plants, consisting of ovary, style and stigma. It may be simple with one carpel or compound consisting of several carpels.

Pollen grain – the microspores (male gametes) of plants.

Pollen mother cell – the cell that will undergo meiosis to produce cells that will become pollen grains.

Pollen sacs – the sporangia in which the microspores, or pollen grains, are produced.

Pollination – the transfer of pollen by wind, water, insects, or birds from the anther to the receptive stigma. (Compare with fertilisation).

Polypetalous – having many separate petals.

Polysepalous – having many separate sepals.

Proboscis – a complicated feeding structure consisting of several mouthparts that are brought together to form a water or nectar sucking apparatus in bees.

Propolis – resinous material collected by bees from plants and used for a variety of purposes in their colonies.

Protandrous – where the anthers mature before the stigma.

Protogynous – where the stigma matures before the anther.

Queenright – a colony is said to be queenright when it has a queen either as a laying adult, a virgin queen or a queen cell present.

Rachis – the axis (not the stalk) of an inflorescence or pinnate leaf.

Receptacle – the usually expanded, often cup-shaped or tubular apical part of a pedicel on which the flower parts are inserted.

Self-fertile – fertilisation of male and female gametes from the same individual to produce viable offspring.

Self-incompatibility – inability for male and female gametes from the same individual to produce viable offspring.

Self-pollination – the transfer of pollen from the anther to the stigma of the same flower, or to the stigma of another flower on the same plant.

Sensillae – sense organs of honey bees located in or under the cuticle with hairs, pegs or plates exposed to the exterior. The sensillae are specialised and each type reacts to a particular stimulus e.g. gravity, touch, strain, movement, taste, carbon dioxide, chemicals, light intensity and polarised light.

Sepal – a part of the calyx of dicotyledenous flowers, usually green and leaf-like.

Sepaloid – like a sepal.

Sessile – without a stalk.

Sexine – the outer layer of the exine of a pollen grain, usually sculptured and providing important features that are used in the identification of pollen grains.

Soil pH – the concentration of hydrogen ions in the water surrounding soil particles. A value less than 7 indicates acidity, and above 7 alkaline conditions. pH 7 is neutral.

Species – the basic unit of classification, sometimes incorrectly referred to as varieties.

Spermatheca – storage organ found only in the queen bee abdomen where she stores the sperm gained during her mating flights and which she will use to fertilise eggs during her life time.

Spermatozoa – sperm in animals.

Subspecies – variants or races of species that are distinctive.

Stamen – the male organ of the flower which produces the pollen grains (microspores) and comprises a stalk bearing the anther at the top.

Staminode – a sterile stamen.

Standard – the erect, expanded fifth petal of a flower of the legume families.

Sternotribic – flowers adapted to deposit pollen on the underside of a pollinating insect whilst visiting the flower.

Stigma – the apical part of the gynoecium that is receptive to pollen.

Stipules – small, usually leaf-like appendages, found on either side of a leaf stalk.

Style – the stalk on any ovary bearing the stigma(s).

Tarsus – the fifth segment of an insect leg.

Thalamus – another name for the receptacle of a flower.

Thermonasty – a response in a flower to a general, non-directional temperature stimulus.

Tibia – the fourth segment of an insect leg.

Torus – another name for the receptacle of a flower.

Trichome – single or many-celled outgrowth from an epidermal plant cell.

Varroa *(varroasis)* – a mite that is parasitic to honey bees. In the UK the species is *Varroa destructor* and requires intensive, integrated pest management control techniques to keep it under control in honey bee colonies.

Vascular system – tissue in plants that carries liquids around the plant.

Versatile – term used to describe where anther lobes are attached to the filament in such a way that they can swing freely, usually found in wind pollinated flowers.

Wax glands – single layers of cells that secrete beeswax from four pairs of glands situated in the underside of the worker abdomen.

Whorl – the arrangement of organs, e.g. flower parts, in a circle around the axis.

Xylem – conducting tissue, also providing mechanical support in stems and roots.

Zygomorphic – flowers that are bilaterally symmetrical (i.e. one plane of symmetry).

GLOSSARY

Selected Reading

Akeroyd, J. (1999) *The Encyclopaedia of Wild Flowers.* (Dempsey Parr)

Bricknell, C. ed. (1990) *The Royal Horticultural Society Gardener's Encyclopedia of Plants and Flowers.* (C Dorling Kindersley)

Chicheley Plowden, C. (1968) *A Manual of Plant Names.* (George Allen and Unwin Ltd)

Clapham, A.R.; Tutin, T.G. and Warburg, E.F. (1962) *Flora of the British Isles.* Second edition. (Cambridge University Press)

Crane, E. (1980) *A Book of Honey.* (Oxford University Press)

Crane, E. (1990) *Bees and Beekeeping.* (Heinemann Newnes)

Dade, H.A. (1985) *Anatomy and Dissection of the Honeybee.* (IBRA)

Davis, C. F. (2004) *The Honey Bee Inside Out.* (Bee Craft Ltd)

Delaplane, K.S. and Mayer, D.F. (2000) *Crop Pollination by Bees.* (CABI Publishing)

Fitter, R.S. and Fitter, A. (2002) *Rapid changes in flowering time in British plants.* Science 296, pp 1689-1691

Gates, P. (2002) *Gardening in the Global Greenhouse: Summary Report.* (UK Climatic Impacts Programme)

Goodman, L. (2003) *Form and Function in the Honey Bee.* (IBRA)

Grigson, G. (1955) *The Englishman's Flora.* (Phoenix House)

Hickey, M. and King, C. (1997) *Common Families of Flowering Plants.* (Cambridge University Press)

Hodges, D. (1984) *The Pollen Loads of the Honey Bee.* (IBRA)

Hooper, T. and Taylor, M. (1988) *The Beekeeper's Garden.* (Alphabooks A&C Black)

Howes, F.N. (1979) *Plants and Beekeeping.* (Faber Paperbacks)

Keble Martin, W. (1965) *The Concise British Flora in Colour.* 3rd impression. (Ebury Press Michael Joseph)

Kirk, W. (1994) *A colour guide to pollen loads of the honey bee.* (IBRA)

Mabey, R. (1996) *Flora Britannica.* (Sinclair Steveson)

Mace, H. (1949) *Bees, Flowers and Fruit.* (The Beekeeping Annual Office Harlow Essex)

Meeuse, B. and Morris, S. (1984) *The Sex life of flowers.* (Faber and Faber London. Boston)

O'Toole, C. and Raw, A. (1993) *Bees of the World.* (Blandford Press)

Page, M. (2001) *Name That Plant. An illustrated Guide to Plant and Botanical Names.* (Worth Press)

Percival, M. (1965) *Floral Biology.* (Pergamon Press)

Preston, C.D; Telfer, M.G.; Arnold, H.; Carey, P.D.; Cooper, J.M.; Dines, T.D.; Hill, M.O.; Pearman, D.A.; Roy, D.B. and Smart, S.M. (2002) *The Changing Flora of the UK.* (London Defra)

Prŷs – Jones, O.E. and Corbet, S.A. (1987) *Bumblebees.* (Cambridge University Press)

Sawyer, R. (1981) *Pollen Identification for Beekeepers.* (Cardiff Academic Press)

Sawyer, R. (1988) *Honey Identification.* (Cardiff Academic Press)

Schneider, S.S. and Lewis, L.A. (2003) *Honey Bee Communication: The "Tremble Dance", the "Vibration Dance" and the "Migration Dance".* Monographs in Honey Bee Biology Number 1, (Northern Bee Books UK)

Seeley, T.D. (1995) *The Wisdom of the Hive. The Social Physiology of Honey Bee Colonies.* (Harvard University Press)

Snodgrass, R.E. (1984) *Anatomy of the Honey Bee.* (Comstock Publishing Associates, Ithaca and London)

Stace, C. (1997) *New Flora of the British Isles.* Second edition. (Cambridge University Press)

Thain, M. and Hickman, M. (1996) *The Penguin Dictionary of Biology.* 9th edition. (Penguin Books)

Von Frisch, K. (1954) *The Dancing Bees.* (Methuen & Co. Ltd. London)

Winston, M. (1987) *The Biology of the Honey Bee.* (Harvard University Press)

Annex I

SOME PLANT FAMILIES USED BY HONEY BEES, WITH NOTES ON THEIR NECTARIES

Aceracae (Acer family) e.g. Sycamore *(Acer pseudoplatanus)*. Nectar is secreted by thick fleshy central disc, freely exposed.

Apiaceae (Umbelliferae) (Carrot family) e.g. Carrot *(Daucus carota)*. Markedly protandrous, nectar secreted by epigynous disc easily accessible.

Arialaceae (Ivy family) e.g. Ivy *(Hedera helix)*. In ivy the nectar is secreted from yellowish-green disc surrounding the styles and is freely exposed.

Asteraceae (Daisy family) e.g. Daisy *(Bellis perennis)*; Dandelion *(Taraxacum officinalis)*; Thistles *(Carduus spp.)*; Sunflower *(Helianthus annus)*. The corolla tube is usually short enough to enable the nectar secreted by a ring-like nectary at the base of the style to be reached. In longer-tubed flowers the corolla tubes are narrow and the nectar rises in them and is accessible.

Boraginaceae (Borage family) e.g. Forget-me-not *(Myosotis spp.)*; Borage *(Borago officinalis)*; Common Comfrey *(Symphytum officinale)*; Lungwort *(Pulmonaria officinalis)*.
Pendulous flowers, nectar secreted by a nectar disc at the base of the ovary.

Brassicaceae (Cruciferae) (Cabbage family) e.g. Aubretia *(Aubretia deltoidea)*; Oil-Seed Rape *(Brassica napus ssp.oleifera)*; Turnip *(Brassica rapa)*; Sweet Alison *(Lobularia maritima)*; Charlock *(Sinapis arvensis)*; Thale Cress *(Arabidopsis thaliana)*; Candytuft *(Iberis spp.)*; Wallflower *(Cheiranthus cheiri)*; Cabbage *(Brassica oleracea)*. Nectaries are small green glands situated on the torus at the base of the short stamens. The nectar gathers in the pouches of lateral sepals. Each flower has four nectaries, two at the base of the short stamens, these secrete much more nectar, of a higher sugar concentration than the two nectaries situated outside the ring of stamens.

Campanulaceae (Bellflower family) e.g. Giant Bellflower *(Campanula latifolia)*. Flowers are markedly protandrous. Nectar is secreted by a disc developed on top of the ovary and is protected by the triangular bases of the stamens.

Caprifoliaceae (Honeysuckle family) Honeysuckle *(Lonicera spp.)*; American elderberry *(Sambucus canadensis)*. Fleshy nectar disc at the base of the corolla tube.

Caryophyllaceae (Pink family) e.g. White Campion *(Silene latifolia)*; Stitchwort *(Stellaria spp.)*. Nectar is secreted at the base of the stamens, often protandrous.

Dipsacaceae (Teasel family) e.g. Scabious *(Knautia arvensis)*; Teasel *(Dipsacus spp.)*. Nectar is secreted on the upper part of the ovary and protected from rain by hairs lining the corolla tube.

Ericaceae (Heather family) e.g. Ling Heather *(Calluna vulgaris)*; Bell Heather *(Erica cinerea)*; Cross-Leaved Heath *(Erica tetralix)*. Flowers are often pendulous. Usually protandrous. Well developed nectar disc at the base of the ovary. Eight tiny swellings that alternate with the bases of the stamens. *E. cinerea* and *E. tetralix* – bees visit the pendulous flowers and first touch the projecting stigma and then shake the anthers by pushing past their appendages. *C. vulgaris* - often wind pollinated as the pollen tetrads are dry and readily blown out of the anthers.

Fabaceae (Leguminoseae) Pea family e.g. Red Clover *(Trifolium pratense)*; White Clover *(Trifolium repens)*; Sweet Pea *(Lathyrus odoratus)*; Broad Bean *(Vicia faba)*; Gorse *(Ulex gallii)*. In species where nectar is produced it is secreted between the base of the stamen tube and the ovary.

Geraniaceae (Crane's-bill family) e.g. Bloody Cranesbill *(Geranium sanguineum)*; Dusky Crane's bill *(Geranium phaeum)*. Protandrous. Five nectar glands representing a disc are found as little cushions just outside the bases of antisepalous stamens.

Grossulariaceae (Gooseberry family) e.g. Gooseberry *(Ribes uva-crispa)*; Blackcurrant *(Ribes nigrum)*. Bell-shaped flower approx 5 mm deep, bee extracts nectar from the open flower. Nectar is secreted at the base of the bell–shaped receptacle and is protected by stiff hairs projecting vertically from the style.

Hydrophyllaceae (Phacelia family) e.g. Phacelia *(Phacelia tanacetifolia)*. The nectary is a disc at the base of the ovary protected by special appendages at the base of the stamens (no hindrance to honey bees).

Lamiaceae (Labiatae) (Dead–nettle family) e.g. Lavender *(Lavandula x intermedia)*; Cat-mint *(Nepeta cataria)*; Rosemary *(Rosmarinus officinalis)*; Thyme *(Thymus spp.)*; Mint *(Mentha spp.)*; Salvia (Claries) *(Salvia spp.)*. Flowers usually protandrous. Nectar disc is at the base of the ovary and is better developed on the anterior side.

Liliaceae (Lily family) e.g. Crocus *(Crocus spp.)*; Lilies *(Lilium spp.)*; Hyacinth *(Hyacynthus orientalis)*; Tulip *(Tulipa gesneriana)*; Onion *(Allium spp.)*; Snowdrop *(Galanthus nivalis)*. In the crocus nectar is secreted by a nectary on top of the ovary. In the bluebell *(Hyacinthoides non-scripta)*, nectar is secreted in glandulous tissue in the partition between the chambers of the ovary, whilst in the tulip there is no nectar and flowers are visited only for pollen. In the hyacinth nectar is secreted as large drops from each of three nectaries appearing as dots near the top of the ovary.

Malvaceae (Mallow family) e.g. Garden Tree Mallow *(Lavatera olbia)*; Mallow *(Malva spp.)*; Hollyhock *(Alcea rosea)*. Nectar is secreted by the torus in five little pits lying between the bases of the petals and protected by hairs.

Onagraceae (Willowherb family) e.g. Willowherbs *(Epilobium spp.)*; Rosebay willowherb *(Chamaenerion angustifolium)*; Evening Primrose *(Oenothera biennis)*. Nectar disc is at the top of the ovary.

Primulaceae (Primrose family) Primose *(Primula vulgaris)*. Nectar secreted around the base of the ovary.

Ranunculaceae (Buttercup family) e.g. Bulbous Buttercup *(Ranunculus bulbosus)*; Wood Anemone *(Anemone nemorosa)*; Winter Aconite *(Eranthis hyemalis)*; Traveller's-joy *(Clematis vitalbis)*; Pasque Flower *(Anemone pulsatilla)*; Marsh Marigold *(Caltha palustris)*; Hellebore *(Helleborus spp.)*. Nectary at the base of the carpels. In Winter Aconites the petals are reduced to hornlike structures with an oblique mouth in which nectar is secreted. In Delphinium nectar is secreted at the bottom of a long spur and can only be reached by long-tongued bees. In Buttercups the nectary is at the base of the flower and is covered by a scale. In the Wood Anemone there are no nectaries, as also is the case in Traveller's-joy. In the Christmas Rose *(Helleborus niger)* there are numerous slipper shaped nectaries.

Rosaceae (Rose family) e.g. Rose *(Rosa spp.)*; Hawthorn *(Crataegus monogyna)*; Raspberry *(Rubus idaeus)*; Blackberry *(Rubus fruticosus)*; Almond *(Prunus dulcis)*; Plum *(Prunus domesticus)*; Wild Cherry *(Prunus avium)*; Cherry Laurel *(Prunus laurocerasus)*; Peach *(Prunus persica)*; Strawberry *(Fragaria spp.)*; Dwarf Cherry *(Prunus cerasus)*. Flowers of the open type e.g. Wild Rose / Strawberry / Raspberry / Apple / Cherry / Rowan and Hawthorn; in most cases nectar is produced by the whole inner surface of the torus or there is a ring-like nectary around the torus mouth within the insertion of the stamens.

- + or - protogynous   apple, hawthorn, sloe
- homogamous   common cherry
- protandrous   roses

Self-pollination is apparently possible in all cases. In the case of the Crab Apple *(Malus pumila)* nectar is secreted inside the calyx tube. In Raspberry it is secreted in a fleshy ring on the margin of the flower within the stamens. No nectar is secreted in the flowers of many Wild Roses (although they produce abundant pollen) with the exception of the Sweet Briar *(Rosa rubigenosa)* where a thin layer of nectar is secreted on the broad fleshy margin of the receptacle or calyx tube.

Salicaceae (Willow family) e.g. Poplar *(Populus spp.)*; Willow *(Salix spp.)*. Both wind and insect pollinated. Goat Willow *(Salix caprea)* female flowers have a nectary. Other species have nectaries on both sexes of flowers.

Scrophulariaceae (Figwort family) e.g. Foxglove *(Digitalis purpurea)*; Common Figwort *(Scrophularia nodosa)*; Mullein *(Verbascum spp.)*. Slightly protandrous and in most cases self-pollination can occur. Nectar disc is at the base of the ovary / corolla.

Thymelaeaceae (Mezereon family) e.g. Daphne *(Daphne spp.)*. Here the nectar is secreted at the base of the ovary

Violaceae (Violet family) e.g. Violas *(Viola spp.)*. In the case of Heart's-ease

(Viola tricolor) the lower petal becomes a spur into which nectar is secreted. The anther of each of the lower stamens has a nectar secreting area which projects into the spur of the lower petal. The two antero-lateral stamens bear greenish horn-like appendages projecting into the spur of the anterior petal and functioning as nectaries.

Annex II

METHODS FOR PREPARING SLIDES OF
POLLEN GRAIN

COLLECTION OF POLLEN GRAINS FOR IDENTIFICATION

Sources
Pollen can be gathered directly from the anthers of flowers, (method 1) from the corbicular loads of the honey bees returning to the hive, (method 2) and extracted from honey (method 3).

Flowers
Flowers collected directly from the plant may have anthers that have not fully opened and so it is worthwhile placing the cuttings in water, indoors for 2 hours, so the anthers ripen fully and dehisce to release their pollen.

Pollen load
The simplest method is to use special pollen traps that are fitted to the front of beehives, however these are expensive and you may not have hives you can use. Instead it is possible to gather smaller quantities directly from the bees themselves as they return to the hives (take care and wear protective clothing to reduce the risk of being stung).

METHOD 1 POLLEN COLLECTED FROM FLOWERS USING GLYCERINE JELLY SMEAR TECHNIQUE AND STAINED WITH AQUEOUS SAFRANIN

Chemicals
- Absolute isoPropanol
- Glycerine jelly
- Aqueous Safranin stain
- Water
- Aqueous mountant (50% glycerine)
- Sealant

Apparatus
- A very fine pipette for isoPropanol
- A very fine pipette for water

- A glass rod for safranin stain
- A very fine glass rod for aqueous mountant (50% glycerine)
- 2 x 15 ml bottles for storing rods after use
- 500 ml measuring cylinder
- 175 ml waste bottle
- Microslides and No. 1.5 coverglasses
- Very fine straight forceps or seeker
- Filter paper or pieces of paper towel
- Compound microscope with at least x400 magnification

Transfering the pollen

1 Place a drop of the melted glycerine jelly on a slide and smear to cover the slide using the tip of a clean finger.
2 Transfer a smear from this smear onto the centre of a number of slides.
3 Put a label on the side of the slide on which the smear has been made.
4 These slides can be stored in a suitable box until required. The smears remain tacky for two to three weeks.
5 The pollen can be transferred from the ' flower onto the smear either in the field or at home.
6 The slides with the pollen on the smears can be stored in the box until time is available to stain them.

Staining the pollen

1 Hold the slide, pollen side uppermost, over the waste bottle and using a very fine glass pipette allow drops of isoPropanol to run onto the pollen and down into the waste bottle. This will dewax the pollen.
2 Using a rod put a drop of the safranin stain onto the alcohol wetted pollen.
3 Stain for 30 seconds or until the area of pollen on the slide can be seen to be red.
4 Wash off excess stain with water into the waste bottle, using water applied from a very fine glass pipette. Too heavy staining can obscure details, whereas light staining will often reveal features not easily observed otherwise.
5 The stained, water–wetted pollen may be examined microscopically at this stage, but it must not be allowed to dry out. Keep it moist with water. Care should be taken not to plunge the objective of the microscope into the stained preparation!
6 The staining process may be repeated if the pollen is understained.

Mounting the pollen

1 Using a small piece of paper towel or filter paper, wipe off excess stain and water from the slide, leaving the water-wetted pollen at the centre of the slide.
2 Lower the tip of the very fine rod vertically into the aqueous mountant. Lift the rod out of the mountant and allow the drop of mountant to run off the rod onto the pollen. Never dip the rod fully into the mountant
3 Using the forceps, or a seeker, hold a coverglass (also known as a coverslip) and lower it so it contacts centrally onto the drop of mountant. The

mountant will then run outwards until it fully covers the area of the coverglass, with little or no mountant on the outside of the coverglass. Aqueous mountant is a very viscous medium and the correct size of drop needed is only found by experience.

Sealing the pollen mount

The mountant will harden in a few hours, or overnight and then a ring of sealant can be applied to overlap the edge of the coverglass and onto the slide. Note there are different sealing systems that can be used.

METHOD 2 SLIDE PREPARATION USING POLLEN LOADS

Chemicals

* 50% glycerol solution
* Pre-prepared safranin stained glyerine jelly
* Paraffin wax or alternative sealant

Apparatus (as in method 1)

Method

1 Select a pollen load and place it on a clean microscope slide.
2 Add a drop or two of the 50% glycerol solution and mix to a uniform slurry.
3 Using a cube 1mm^3 of stained glycerine jelly on the end of a pin or needle, touch the pollen slurry to pick up a small amount. Do not pick up too much of the mixture as there will be too many grains visible under the microscope to discern adequate detail.
4 Gently heat the slide stirring the pollen/jelly mix with a glass rod when melted. Add a cover slip carefully pressing down a little if the depth between the slide and slip is too thick.
5 Seal with paraffin wax or alternative sealant.
6 Label with preparation date, adding pollen details after examination.

Pollen grain size can be affected by the ways in which they are prepared for examination under the microscope. In calibrating the slide the standard of hazel is often used, as the pollen grains of hazel are quite consistently 25 microns in size.

METHOD 3 SEDIMENTATION TECHNIQUE
FOR MELISSOPALYNOLOGY

Method

Where a centrifuge is not available, this simple sedimentation method can be used.

1 Weigh 20 g of a honey sample and place in a 50 ml measuring cylinder. Add water to 50 ml level. Carefully stir ensuring the honey is well dissolved.
2 Allow to stand undisturbed for a minimum of 6 hours or overnight.
3 Very carefully pour off as much of the liquid as possible without disturbing

the sediment too much. Allow a little more liquid to remain if it proves difficult not to agitate the sediment; this can be allowed to evaporate later.

4   Using a small pipette extract as much of the sediment as is possible and transfer it, spread very thinly onto microscope slides already prepared with a very fine smear of glycerine jelly.

5   The procedure described in method 1 for staining / sealing slides can then be followed.

Equipment for these techiques can be obtained from specialist suppliers of microscopes and specimen preparation materials.

Annex III

RECOMMENDED WILDFLOWER AND GRASS SEED MIXTURES TO BENEFIT BEES ON FIELD MARGINS OR GRASSLAND SITES OF SPECIFIC SOIL TYPES

CULTIVATION NOTES

The following mixtures can be sown in field margins or blocks. Ideally a few blocks of up to 1 ha scattered around the farm / land under management. The seed should be broadcast and rolled rather than drilled.

Glyphosate may be applied as an overall spray immediately before spring sowing, in order to help establish the crop. Otherwise, limit herbicide application to weed wiper or spot treatment, or cut occasionally in the first year, if necessary to prevent weeds dominating.

All of the sown areas should be cut after 15 September, at a height of 10–20 cm, ideally removing the cuttings using a forage harvester. Then each year, cut the same half of the area before the end of June to stimulate late flowering, unless there are ground-nesting birds present, and repeat the total cut in September. The legumes in these mixes should last 3-5 years before re-sowing may be necessary.

Where appropriate, extensive autumn and winter grazing of cattle produces optimal conditions for bumblebee forage plants to flower in the following spring by accelerating nutrient removal, and limiting the ability of competitive species dominance. Cattle are better than sheep in producing a more species diverse sward. Well-established, closer swards are even better for providing more suitable bee nest sites.

NEUTRAL / LOAMY SOILS

COMMON NAME	BOTANICAL NAME	FLOWERING PERIOD
WILD FLOWERS		
Knapweed	*Centaurea nigra*	July–September
Meadow Geranium	*Geranium pratense*	April–October
Field Scabious	*Knautia arvensis*	June–September
Oxeye Daisy	*Leucanthemum vulgare*	June–August
Bird's-Foot-Trefoil	*Lotus corniculatus*	June–August
Self-Heal	*Prunella vulgaris*	May–October
Meadow Buttercup	*Ranunculus acris*	May–July
Yellow Rattle	*Rhinanthus minor*	May–August
Red Clover	*Trifolium pratense*	May–October
Alsike Clover	*Trifolium hybridum*	May–October
Tufted Vetch	*Vicia cracca*	June–August

GRASSES	
Common Bent	*Agrostis capillaris*
Sweet Vernal-grass	*Anthoxanthum odoratum*
Crested Dog's-tail	*Cynosurus cristatus*
Sheep's Fescue	*Festuca ovina*
Chewings' Fescue	*Festuca rubra spp. commutata*
Yellow Oat-grass	*Trisetum flavescens*

CALCAREOUS SOILS

COMMON NAME	BOTANICAL NAME	FLOWERING PERIOD
WILD FLOWERS		
Kidney vetch	*Anthyllis vulneraria*	
Knapweed	*Centaurea nigra*	June–September
Greater Knapweed	*Centaurea scabiosa*	July–September
Wild Basil	*Clinopodium vulgare*	July–August
Field Scabious	*Knautia arvensis*	July–September
Oxeye daisy	*Leucanthemum vulgare*	June–September
Bird's-foot-trefoil	*Lotus corniculatus*	June–August
Musk Mallow	*Malva moschata*	June–August
Rest-harrow	*Ononis repens*	July–September
Marjoram	*Origanum vulgare*	June–September
Self-Heal	*Prunella vulgaris*	July–October
Meadow Buttercup	*Ranunculus acris*	May–October
Yellow Rattle	*Rhinanthus minor*	May–July
Red clover	*Trifolium pratense*	May–August
Tufted vetch	*Vicia cracca*	May–October

GRASSES

Common Bent	*Agrostis capillaris*
Crested Dog's-tail	*Cynosurus cristatus*
Sheep's Fescue	*Festuca ovina*
Chewing's Fescue	*Festuca rubra spp. commutata*
Timothy Grass	*Phleum pratense*
Yellow Oat-grass	*Trisetum flavescens*

ACIDIC / SANDY SOILS

COMMON NAME	BOTANICAL NAME	FLOWERING PERIOD
WILDFLOWERS		
Knapweed	*Centaurea nigra*	July–September
Viper's Bugloss	*Echium vulgare*	June–September
Oxeye Daisy	*Leucanthemum vulgare*	June–August
Common Toadflax	*Linaria vulgaris*	July–October
Bird's-Foot-Trefoil	*Lotus corniculatus*	June–August
Musk Mallow	*Malva moschata*	July–September
Self-Heal	*Prunella vulgaris*	May–October
Yellow Rattle	*Rhinanthus minor*	May–August
Betony	*Stachys officinalis*	June–August
Red Clover	*Trifolium pratense*	May–October
Common Vetch	*Vicia sativa*	May–July

GRASSES		
Common Bent	*Agrostis capillaris*	
Sweet Vernal-grass	*Anthoxanthum odoratum*	
Crested Dog's-tail	*Cynosurus cristatus*	
Wavy Hair-grass	*Deschampsia flexuosa*	
Sheep's Fescue	*Festuca ovina*	
Red Fescue	*Festuca rubra*	

WET SOILS

COMMON NAME WILDFLOWERS	BOTANICAL NAME	FLOWERING PERIOD
Knapweed		July–September
Meadowsweet	*Centaurea nigra*	June–September
Greater Bird's-foot-trefoil	*Filipendula ulmaria*	June–August
Ragged-Robin	*Lotus pedunculatus*	May–August
Betony	*Lychnis flos-cuculi*	June–August
Marsh Woundwort	*Stachys officinalis*	June–August
Self-Heal	*Stachys palustris*	May–October
Devil's-Bit Scabious	*Prunella vulgaris*	July–August
Red Clover	*Succisa pratensis*	May–October
	Trifolium pratense	
GRASSES		
Meadow or Common Fox-tail	*Alopecurus pratensis*	
Sweet Vernal-grass	*Anthoxanthum odoratum*	
Tufted Hair-grass	*Deschampsia cespitosa*	
Red Fescue	*Festuca rubra*	

ANNEX III

Annex IV

TREES FOR HONEY BEES

TREE SPECIES	APPROX. FLOWERING TIMES						
	Jan	Feb	Mar	Apr	May	June	July
ACERS				•	•		
Acer platanoides Norway Maple							
Acer palmatum Japanese Maple							
Acer campestris Field Maple							
Acer pseudoplatanus Sycamore							
ALDERS (Pollen only)	•	•	•				
Alnus cordata Italian Alder							
Alnus glutinosa Common Alder							
Alnus incana Grey Alder							
APPLES				•	•		
Malus domestica							
BUCKTHORN					•	•	
Rhamnus catharticus							
CRAB APPLES				•	•		
Malus sylvestris							
Malus hupehensis							
Malus pumila							
HAWTHORNS					•		
Crataegus monogyna							
Crataegus laevigata Midland Hawthorn							
Crateagus spp. (select single flowered varieties)							
Crateagus crus-galli, mollis, phaenopyrum, pinnatifida							
HAZEL (pollen only)	•	•	•				
Corylus avellana Hazel / Cobnut							
HOLLY					•	•	
Ilex aquifolium							

TREE SPECIES Continued   FLOWERING TIMES

	Jan	Feb	Mar	Apr	May	June	July
HORSE-CHESTNUTS				•	•	•	
Aesculus hippocastanum Horse-chestnut							
Aesculus carnea Red Horse-chestnut							
Aesculus indica Indian Horse-chestnut							
LIMES						•	•
Tilia cordata Small-leaved Lime							
Tilia platyphyllos Broad-leaved Lime							
Tilia euchloria Caucasian Lime							
PEAR				•	•		
Pyrus pyraster Wild Pear							
POPLARS (Pollen only)	•	•					
Populus nigra Black Poplar							
Populus canescens Grey Poplar							
Populus tremula Aspen							
PRUNUS			•	•	•		
Prunus avium Wild Cherry / Gean							
Prunus padus Bird Cherry							
Prunus spinosa Blackthorn / Sloe							
Prunus amygdalis Almond							
Prunus armeniaca Apricot							
Prunus cerasus Cherry							
Prunus persica Peach							
Prunus laurocerasus Cherry Laurel							
Prunus lusitanica Portugal Laurel							
ROWAN					•	•	
Sorbus aucuparia Rowan							
Sorbus aria Whitebeam							
SWEET CHESTNUT						•	
Castanea sativa Spanish /Sweet Chestnut							
WILLOWS		•	•	•			
Salix alba White Willow							
Salix fragilis Crack Willow							
Salix cinerea Sallow							
Salix caprea Goat Willow							

Annex V

SHRUBS, PLANTS & WILDFLOWERS FOR HONEY BEES

SHRUBS
N and P mean nectar and pollen sources respectively

Abelia N/P (May – August) full sun, requires good drainage
Abelia chinensis
Abelia schumanii

Barberry N/P (April – July) full sun, semi-shade, tolerates most soils
Berberis spp.
B.buxifolia
B. darwinii
B. thunbergii

Buddleia N only (May – September) full sun, lime tolerant,
B.globosa loamy soils, dry
B.alternifolia
B. davidii

Ceanothus spp. N/P (May – October) full sun best on lime-free soils
C. thyrsiflorus
C.burkwoodii

Cotoneaster spp. N/P (May-June) full sun, or semi-shade , salt tolerant,
garden soils
C.horizontalis

Escallonia N/P (June – October) full sun, salt tolerant, well drained soils
E. bifida

Eucryphia spp N/P (July – September) full sun or semi-shade, light
neutral/acid soils

Hebe N only (June – October) full sun, salt tolerant, well drained soils
H. macroantha
H. cupressoides

Ivy N/P (October/November) full sun or semi-shade, any soils
H. helix
H. colchica

Mahonia N/P (March and April) full sun or semi-shade, good garden soil
M. aquifolium
Portugal Laurel N only (June) full sun or semi-shade, well drained soil
Prunus lusitanica
Rosemary N/P (March – September) full sun, dry, well drained,
Rosmarinus officinalis salt tolerant
Rose P only (June-October) full sun, well drained soils
Rosa spp. (single and semi double flowered)
Skimmia N/P (March-April) semi-shade, salt tolerant,
(Note dioecious)
Skimmia japonica
Snowberry N/P (July – September) full sun or semi-shade, well drained soil
Symphoricarpos albus
Willow N/P (March – April) full sun or semi-shade, moist soil
Salix lanata
S. gracilistyla

PLANTS AND WILDFLOWERS
Aconite Winter (Jan-Feb) Full sun is the optimum situation
Eranthis hyemalis
Alkanet N only (June-August) full sun, damp woods
Anchusa officinalis
Alyssum N/P (May – Oct) full sun
Alyssum maritima syn. Lobularia maritima
Arabis N/P (March onwards) full sun / semi shade
*Arabis spp. (*various varieties)
Aubretia N/P (April-May) full sun
Aubretia spp.
Bellflower N/P (May – October) full sun or semi-shade, rock gardens,
Campanula spp. well drained soil
Blackberry N/P (May-September) full sun or semi-shade, hedgerows
Rubus fruticosus
Borage N/P (June – September) full sun or semi-shade, well drained soil
Borago officinalis
Catnip N/P (May – September) full sun, dry well drained soil
Nepeta cataria
Celandine N/P (March –May) full sun or semi shade, damp places
Ranunculus ficaria
Clover N/P (May – October) full sun, grassland
Trifolium repens
Cornflower N/P (May – October) full sun
Centaurea cyanus minor

Crane's-bill N/P   (April – October) full sun, well drained soil
Geranium ibericum
G. psilostemon
G. pratense
G. sanguineum
Crocus N/P   (January – February) full sun, well drained soil
Crocus spp.
Dandelion N/P   (March-October) full sun, grassland any soils
Taraxacum officinalis
Dead-Nettle N/P   (February-August) semi-shade, meadows,
          hedge bottoms
Lamium purpureum
Forget-me-not N/P   (May – July) full sun, light soils
Myosotis arvensis
M. scorpoides
Globe Thistle N only   (July – September) full sun, well drained soil
Echinops bannaticus
Echinops exaltatus
Golden rod N/P   (July- October) full sun, dry grassland
Solidago canadensis
Ground Ivy N/P only   (March-June) full sun or semi-shade, hedges, verges
Glechoma hederacea
Hawkbit N/P   (June – September) grassland
Leontodon autumnalis
Hellebore N/P   (late Feb – May) full sun or semi shade
Helleborus niger
H. foetidus
H. viridis
Hemp Agrimony N/P (July-August) damp places
Eupatorium cannabinum
Heathers & Heaths N/P (Year round) full sun or semi-shade, peaty acid soils
Erica spp.
Calluna spp.
Hound's-tongue N/P (June-August) full sun, semi-shade, dry soil, sand
Cynoglossum officinale
Knapweed N/P   (July – September) full sun, dry grassland
Centaurea nigra
Lavender N/P   (May – September) full sun, dry salt tolerant well
          drained soil
Lavandula officinalis
L. stoechas
L. angustifolia
L. x intermedia

Lucerne N/P   (June – July) full sun, grassland and verges
Medicago sativa
Mallow N/P   (June – September) full sun, any soils, verges
Malva sylvestris
Marjoram N/P   (July – September) full sun, well drained soils
Origanum vulgare
Meadowsweet P only (June-September) semi-shade, damp / wet areas
Filipendula ulmaria
Melilot N/P   (July – September) meadows, any soils
Melilotus alba
M. officinalis
Michaelmas Daisies N/P (September – October) full sun, fertile well
Aster spp.   drained soils
Mignonette N/P   (June-August) dry pasture, hedge bottoms
Roseda odorata
Milkwort N/P   (May-June) full sun , chalky soils
Polygala vulgaris
Phacelia N/P   (July)   full sun, well cultivated damp conditions
Phacelia tanacetifolia
Poached egg plant N/P (May – September), full sun, requires cool conditions
Limnanthes douglasii   for roots
Poppy P only   (May – August) full sun, well drained soils
Papaver alpinum
P. nudicaule
P. rhoeas
Purple-loosestrife N/P (June – September) full sun or semi-shade, damp soils
Lythrum (Lysimachia) salicaria
Rock Rose N/P   (June – July) full sun, dry and salt tolerant,
                           well–drained soil
Helianthemum nummularium
Rosebay willowherb N/P (July – September) full sun or semi shade, all soils
Epilobium (Chamerion) angustifolium
E. hirsutum
Sage N/P   (May-July) full sun, prefers a dry soil
Salvia officinalis
Sainfoin N/P   (June - August) chalky soils full sun
Onobrychis viciifolia
Scabious N/P   (June – October) full sun, damp places
Knautia arvensis

Sedum N only   (June – October) full sun, dry, well drained conditions
Sedum spp.

Teasel N only   (July –September) full sun, semi shade, any soil
Dipsacus fullonum

Thistle N/P   (May-August) full sun or semi shade any soil
Cirsium arvense

Thyme N only   (May-August) full sun, dry, prefers chalky soils
Thymus serpyllum
T. vulgaris
T. praecox

Toadflax N/P   (July- October) full sun, grassland
Linaria vulgaris

Traveller's-joy P only (July) full sun, prefers chalky/alkaline soils
Clematis vitalba

Trefoil N/P   (June – August) full sun, grassland
Lotus corniculatus
Trifolium campestre
Medicago lupulina

Vetch N   (April-July) full sun or semi shade, hedgebanks
Vicia sativa   grassland

Violet N only   (April-May) full sun or semi-shade, any soils
Viola odorata

Viper's bugloss N/P (June-September) full sun, grassland
Echium vulgare

Wallflower N/P   (April-June) full sun, salt tolerant, well drained soil
Cheiranthus spp.

White Dead-nettle N/P (March-December) semi-shade, hedgebottoms
Lamium album

Wild Strawberry N/P (April-July) full sun, dry grassland/woodland
Fragaria vesca

Winter cress N/P   (May-June), water stream banks
Barbarea vulgaris

Wood anemone Ponly (July-August), full sun, semi-shade, dry grassland,
Anemone nemorosa   woods

Wood sage N/P   (July-August) full sun, semi shade, dry grassland
Teucrium scorodonia   and woods

ANNEX V

Subject Index

SUBJECT INDEX

Plant Index

Common Name	Binomial Name	Family	Pages
Abelia	*Abelia spp.* *(e.g. chinensis, schumanii)*	Caprifoliaceae	127
Aconite (Winter)	*Eranthis hyemalis*	Ranunculaceae	21, 51, 113, 128
Alder	*Alnus glutinosa*	Betulaceae	54, 82, 93
Alkanet	*Anchusa officinalis*	Boraginaceae	128
Almond	*Prunus amygdalus*	Rosaceae	29, 93, 133, 126
Alsike Clover	*Trifolium hybridum*	Fabaceae	120
Alyssum	*Lobularia maritima*	Brassicaceae	93, 128
American Elderberry	*Sambucus canadensis*	Caprifoliaceae	33, 111
Anchusa	*Anchusa (e.g. azurea, capensis)*	Boraginaceae	93
Apple	*Malus spp. (e.g. sylvestris, domestica)*	Rosaceae	30, 32, 43, 51, 78, 83, 85, 86, 93, 113, 125
Apricot	*Prunus armeniaca*	Rosaceae	83, 85, 126
Aquilegia	*Aquilegia vulgaris*	Ranunculaceae	77
Arabis	*Arabis spp.*	Brassicaceae	93, 128
Ash	*Fraxinus excelsior*	Oleaceae	93
Aspen	*Populus tremula*	Salicaceae	126
Aubergine	*Solanum melongena*	Solanaceae	86
Aubretia	*Aubretia deltoidea*	Brassicaceae	51, 93, 111, 128
Autumn Crocus	*Colchicum autumnale*	Liliaceae	93
Azalea (Yellow)	*Rhododendron luteum*	Ericaceae	78
Balsam	*Impatiens glandulifera*	Balsaminaceae	47, 51, 93
Barberry	*Berberis spp.* *(e.g. buxifolia, darwinii, thunbergii)*	Berberidaceae	93, 127
Beech	*Fagus sylvatica*	Fagaceae	53, 54, 93
Beet leaf / beetroot	*Beta vulgaris ssp. vulgaris*	Chenopodiaceae	87
Bellflowers	*Campanula spp.*	Campanulaceae	111, 128
Bell Heather	*Erica cinerea*	Ericaceae	27, 28, 51, 92, 93, 112
Bergamot	*Monarda didyma*	Lamiaceae	93
Betony	*Stachys officinalis*	Lamiaceae	122, 123
Bilberry	*Vaccinium myrtillus*	Ericaceae	93

PLANT INDEX